'You can't do  walk out on n

'Watch me!' Aidan

Acting purely or
rational thought, India dashed forward,
snatching the bouquet of cream roses from the
grasp of her open-mouthed chief bridesmaid.

'I said no!'

As she spoke she flung the bouquet after him.
With reflexes as swift as a cat's he turned, one
long hand coming out to catch the bouquet just
before it crashed to the ground.

'Well, now,' he drawled lazily, lifting the
flowers in mocking salute. 'I believe that,
traditionally at least, this means that of
everyone here I should be the next person to be
married. Isn't that what's supposed to happen to
whoever catches the bride's bouquet? But
you'll have to forgive me if I prefer to pass on
this particular opportunity…'

Kate Walker was born in Nottinghamshire, but as she grew up in Yorkshire she has always felt that her roots were there. She met her husband at university and orginally worked as a children's librarian, but after the birth of her son she returned to her old childhood love of writing. When she's not working she divides her time between her family, their three cats and her interests of embroidery, antiques, film and theatre, and, of course, reading.

Recent titles by the same author:

HERS FOR A NIGHT
THE UNEXPECTED CHILD

THE GROOM'S REVENGE

BY
KATE WALKER

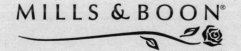
MILLS & BOON®

First published in Great Britain 1997
Harlequin Mills & Boon Limited,
Eton House, 18-24 Paradise Road, Richmond, Surrey TW9 1SR

© Kate Walker 1997

ISBN 0 263 80461 5

Set in Times Roman 10 on 11 pt.
01-9711-60343 C1

Printed and bound in Great Britain
by Mackays of Chatham PLC, Chatham

CHAPTER ONE

'No.'

The single, emphatic syllable was the one word no one was expecting to hear. In the circumstances, it was the last thing any of the congregation in the tiny village church could have anticipated.

It was just one word, but it was enough to shatter the happy, festive atmosphere of what should have been India's most wonderful day and turn it into the worst nightmare she had ever had.

Only seconds before, her uncle, the celebrant, had smiled encouragement at the couple standing before him, his eyes meeting India's green ones through the fine lace of her veil.

'And now we come to the most important point in the service—your vows. Aidan...'

The man at his niece's side had straightened noticeably. His dark head had lifted, his shoulders going back as if in preparation for the responsibility he was about to undertake. The slight movement had drawn India's eyes to him at once. She'd seen the tension stamped onto his face, the tightness of the muscles around his strong jaw. Immediately all her own nerves had vanished, her earlier tremulous smile growing, becoming stronger.

She would never have believed that her husband-to-be would share her own apprehension at this important moment, and the realisation that he did had warmed her heart, making her slide her hand into his at his side. She had been just a little disconcerted to find that Aidan made no response. Instead he had simply let her hand rest where it was, not closing his own strong fingers around it as she had expected.

'Aidan, do you take India to be your wife...?'

The familiar words, heard so many times before at other, far less personally significant moments, had echoed round the small medieval church, seeming to hang in the air along with the delicate scent of the banks of cream and gold flowers that framed the altar.

India's heart had skipped a beat at the thought that the moment she had been waiting for was finally here. In just a few more seconds it would all be official and she would be Aidan's wife, no longer India Marchant but India Wolfe.

'Until death do you part?'

Until death do you part. She would be Aidan's, and he hers for the rest of her life.

The idea was so amazing that it had stopped her thought processes, leaving her unaware of the fact that her uncle was no longer speaking, his ritual question complete.

By the time she'd registered that fact, the silence that had followed had already become just a little too drawn out, too significant to be simply the result of the need to take a steadying breath or impose the necessary control to be able to answer with confidence. The seconds had dragged on and on, extending the wait into a nerve-stretching endurance test.

'Aidan?'

William Marchant's questioning prompt had been echoed by a spontaneous murmur of curious interest from the congregation, crammed into the dark wooden pews in the body of the church. Behind the ornate lace of her veil, India hadn't been able to help smiling to herself at the thought that her family and friends might have anticipated that the bride might find her courage had deserted her at this vital moment, but not the *groom.*

At least, not this particular groom. Aidan Wolfe, the notorious 'Lone Wolfe'; a man with a reputation for being a ruthless businessman with a mind like a steel trap, so unsure of himself that he was lost for words? Never!

'*Aidan*—do you take...?'

'No.'

It came out harshly, almost savagely. The single word slashed through the priest's reiteration of the question with a cold violence that stopped it dead, creating a silence so complete, so taut, that it was as if all the air in the church had suddenly frozen into a sheet of ice, obliterating all sound.

No?

The word rang inside India's head like the stunning aftermath of a violent blow to her skull, and she felt as if all the air had been driven from her lungs, leaving her gasping for breath. He couldn't have said...

No?

Her lips formed the word but no sound came out. With her green eyes wide and dark with shock, her face losing all colour, she could only stare at the man she had come here to marry.

Aidan's hard profile was etched against one of the small, paned windows. His proud, dark head was held high, revealing the strongly carved bone structure that gave his features a power that went far beyond the restrictions of such inadequate descriptions as 'handsome'.

A weak shaft of sunlight slanted through the stained glass, spotlighting his strong, tall frame before falling in a warm, soft pool on the stone flags at his feet. But there was nothing warm or soft about the man himself, the hard lines into which his face was set seeming to be mirrored by the elegant severity of the formal morning dress he wore. Seeing him like this, India suddenly felt as if cold, cruel fingers had gripped her heart and twisted it savagely.

He still hadn't touched her hand, ignoring it where it was linked with his own, and his eyes—eyes she knew to be dark as polished ebony—were obdurately turned away from her, staring deliberately straight ahead. Not even a flicker of a sidelong glance gave any indication of the fact that he was aware of her presence in any way.

'Aidan...'

Clearly uneasy, her uncle tried again, the concern that made his voice rough and uneven scraping over India's already raw nerves so that she had to bite down hard on her lower lip to hold back a cry of distress.

'I said, do you—?'

'And I said *no!*'

At last he moved, swinging round to face India as he spoke. And, seeing his expression, she could only wish that he had kept his head turned away after all.

This wasn't the man she knew! This harsh-featured creature with the burning dark eyes, the blaze of contempt in them searing over her, wasn't the man she had fallen head over heels for.

The savage look that swept over her white face clearly noted the shocking contrast between her colourless cheeks and the fall of long jet-black hair, arranged into ornate curls and topped with a small silver coronet for this special occasion. But no flicker of emotion, no hint of reaction revealed that he was in any way affected by how devastated she looked. For the first time since she had met him, India found that she really understood just why he had been given that rather disturbing nickname.

'Aidan...'

Her use of his name was as shaky as she felt her grasp on reality had become. She didn't even know if the hand that clasped his arm was to draw his attention or to provide herself with some support against the worrying weakness that threatened to overwhelm her. She feared that she might actually collapse in a pile of white silk and antique lace right at his elegantly shod feet.

'Please don't play games...'

It was all she could think of. It had to be some appalling joke, something in unbelievably bad taste, and she tried to force a smile that showed she understood.

It was met with an obdurately hostile glare of rejection, his face so hard and unyielding that she felt as if her gaze had physically slammed into something as solid as a brick wall, and he shook her hand from his arm with a rough movement.

'No game, darling.' His tone turned the endearment into the worst obscenity he could possibly have flung at her. 'I said no, and I meant no.'

In the ranged pews, the gathered guests could only stare in stunned silence. The sombre shock in their expressions seemed suddenly in almost comical contrast to the colourful gaiety of their clothes.

'*Please*—be serious.'

'Never more so, sweetheart,' he assured her with dark flippancy.

'But...'

The scent of the flowers seemed heavier now, rich and oppressive, making her stomach churn nauseously.

'You can't mean...'

'"Can't mean"?' Aidan echoed sardonically. 'What can't I mean, darling? God, do I have to spell it out for you? All right then—'

His hand coming out fast as a striking snake, he caught hold of her wrist, yanking her towards him so roughly that she spun round in a semi-circle, ending up facing the congregation, her back to the altar.

Through unfocused eyes she was aware of her father in the front pew, his round face patched the red of anger and the white of concern as he got to his feet, hastily restrained by her mother's warning hand.

He had never wanted this marriage, she recalled miserably. Initially he had warned her against linking her life with a man of Aidan's background and reputation, but, just lately, swayed by her determination and conviction, he had seemed to come round to the idea. Now she was forced to wish that she had given more weight to his doubts.

'Let's make it absolutely clear. No, *I will not marry you.*'

Each word was delivered with icily brutal precision, the overly clear enunciation aimed at ensuring there could be no possible room for misunderstanding.

'I will not take you for better for worse, in sickness and in health, for richer for poorer—especially not that—or any other of those totally meaningless promises that you were expecting me to mouth so compliantly before all of these persons here present.'

India flinched away from his black parody of the wedding service and the vows they should by now have made if events hadn't taken this appalling, devastatingly unexpected turn, bringing her hopes and dreams falling in tiny pieces around her.

In an act of instinctive self-protection, she tried to lift her hands to cover her ears, only to have Aidan force them down again, ebony eyes blazing harshly into green.

'Listen, damn you! I want you to hear this. I want you to know that I will not marry you now or at any time in the future. I would rather die than surrender myself to such an imprisonment—accede to what I know is no more than the worst form of a lie.'

'But…'

'No!'

Abruptly he released her, dropping her hand as if he felt that to touch her might actually contaminate him in some way. Drawing in a deep, ragged breath, he raked strong fingers violently through the dark silk of his hair, ruffling its shining sleekness.

'I'm sorry, babe, but that's how it's going to be.'

The sunlight brought out the burnished gleam of the coppery strands in the darkness of his hair, the rough movement of his hand making a single lock fall forward over his broad forehead. With the memory of the many occasions on which, in the past, she had been able to smooth such a wayward strand back from his face clear in her mind, she found that her fingers itched to do just that. Perhaps if she could just touch him…

But the set of his face and the cold burn of his eyes shrivelled the idea even as it formed, and suddenly the bitter truth was more than she could bear.

'You're not sorry at all!' she cried sharply, the gnawing pain deep inside biting even harder when a tiny, almost imperceptible inclination of his head seemed to indicate a careless confirmation of her accusation.

'You're not sorry because—because…'

Her throat closed over the words. Because you don't even care. She couldn't bring her tongue to form them, and had to swallow convulsively in order to stop herself from choking on the knot of pain that had formed.

She had always known. Right from the very start of their whirlwind romance, she had known that Aidan's feelings didn't really match hers—not in the fullest sense. He wasn't the one who had been stunned to find that this amazing person, this man who had knocked her so completely off balance, both physically and emotionally, could actually *want* her. So, when he had asked her to marry him, she hadn't thought twice. She had said yes at once, and then had pushed for the wedding to be as soon as possible, terrified he might change his mind.

But how could he do this? How could he just stand there, so cool and calmly collected, when with each word that he spoke he was destroying her world completely?

'Don't do this.' Her voice was low, so fiercely controlled that it sounded almost as cold as his. 'Don't make me hate you.'

'Hate…'

The broad, straight shoulders lifted in a gesture of carelessly contemptuous dismissal.

'I will hate you! I'll hate you with all my heart! If you do this, Aidan, I'll never forgive you—ever!'

He smiled; he actually smiled. But the curve of his lips held no warmth or trace of humour, making his response a bitter mockery of everything it should have meant.

'Fine,' he declared crisply. 'That's just fine with me. In fact, my lovely India, that's exactly the way I want it.'

And with that hateful smile still lingering on his sensual mouth, he turned on his heel and strode away from her, going swiftly down the aisle, his footsteps echoing in the stunned silence.

'*No!*'

With a wild gesture, India flung back the antique lace veil, revealing a pale oval face in which her bright green eyes blazed like burning emeralds above high cheekbones, her normally full, generous mouth drawn tight with tension.

'You can't do this! You can't just walk out on me!'

Aidan spared her a swift, scathing glance over his shoulder.

'Watch me!' he flung at her.

Acting purely on instinct, totally beyond rational thought, India dashed forward, snatching the bouquet of cream roses from the grasp of her open-mouthed chief bridesmaid.

'I said no!'

As she spoke she flung the bouquet after him, watching the gorgeous flowers, chosen so carefully and so happily only a few weeks before, sail through the air, heading straight for Aidan's broad back.

But some intuition of his own, or some movement glimpsed out of the corner of his eye, must have warned him. With reflexes as swift as a cat's he turned, one long hand coming out to catch the bouquet just before it crashed to the ground.

For a long moment there was an intent, brittle silence. Aidan's dark, unreadable eyes clashed with India's over-brilliant green ones over the heads of the congregation, holding her transfixed like some small wild animal frozen in the headlights of an oncoming car. But then Aidan abruptly broke the taut contact. Glancing down at the bouquet he held, he twisted it round consideringly, a thoughtful look on his face. A moment later that reflective expression was replaced by another of those unexpected and far from humorous smiles.

'Well, now,' he drawled lazily, lifting the flowers in mocking salute. 'I believe that, traditionally at least, this means that of everyone here I should be the next person to be married. Isn't that what's supposed to happen to whoever catches the bride's bouquet? But you'll have to forgive me if I prefer to pass on this particular opportunity, or any other that presents itself. You see, the idea of a life of slavery to one woman is not something I can face with any degree of equanimity.'

India couldn't believe what she was hearing. *Life of slavery.* He was talking as if she had trapped him in some way—but he'd been the one who had proposed to her!

And that had definitely not been just a ploy to get her into his bed. There had been no need for that. Physically, there had been no holding back on either part. But then, with Aidan, holding back was something of which she had never been capable.

'But perhaps if you try again you'll have better luck with someone else.'

Disdainfully he tossed the flowers back towards her, deliberately throwing them short so that even if she had made the effort to try to catch them they would still have fallen on the floor at her feet. The impact crushed the delicate blooms against the stone floor, scattering satiny cream petals over the flags.

'You said you wanted to marry a rich man, my darling. But I'm sorry, it isn't going to be me—even if I *was* the first through that door.'

And then she knew. India gave a small, shaken moan of distress, realising exactly what he meant.

'I'm sick and tired of genteel poverty!' Her own foolish words came back to haunt her.

'You just watch me! I'm going to find myself a wealthy husband, one who can keep me in a manner to which I have every intention of becoming accustomed...

'And I don't plan on waiting for him to come to me. In fact, the very next rich man who walks through that door will find himself on the receiving end of such a campaign of seduction and enticement that he won't be able to resist me. I'll bet you anything you like I'll have his ring on my finger before he knows what's hit him…!'

It had been only a joke.

She tried to say the words but they wouldn't form in her mouth, the knowledge that they weren't strictly true closing her throat against them. She had only been half joking when she had made her impetuous declaration at her friend's party—she had been half-serious too.

But when Aidan had walked into the room a short time later anything that had gone before had been forgotten in an instant, driven from her mind by a rush of sensual awareness so overwhelming that she'd been incapable of thinking of anything else.

But how had Aidan heard her crazy bet? He hadn't even been in the house then—had he?

'Aidan…' she tried, but her voice was too weak to carry to him and, looking into the stony, set lines of his face, she knew that even if it had he wouldn't have listened. Her small hesitation had been taken as evidence against her, used as proof of her guilt.

'So I'm sorry.' The dark intonation made it plain that sorrow was the very last thing he was feeling. 'You'll have to make do with what you've got; I have nothing more to give you. But don't give up, darling. There are plenty more fish in the sea.'

One strong, tanned hand swept through the air in a gesture that took in all the congregation—all watching wide-eyed, stunned into stillness and silence by the drama unfolding before them.

Her family, *her* friends, India realised miserably. She had known that Aidan had no family living, and he had claimed that the speed with which their marriage had been arranged meant that his friends couldn't make it to the service. But now she was forced to wonder if in fact he had ever invited them at all. Just how long had he been planning the revenge of this very public rejection?

'I'm sure someone else here would be only too willing to oblige. Just don't expect me to stand around and watch.'

And as soon as he had finished speaking he turned on his heel and strode away from her, walking out of the church and out of her life without so much as a backward glance.

CHAPTER TWO

THE flowers were the first thing that India saw when she let herself into the house at the end of a long, emotionally draining day. Instinctively she knew that they meant trouble, and trouble was something she already had more than enough of on her plate.

The gold and cream beauty of the roses glowed in the late evening sun, their colour in powerful contrast to the deep oak of the dresser on which they lay. They were glorious—there was no other word for them. A sight that would normally lift anyone's spirits.

But it wasn't the present bouquet that registered in India's thoughts. Instead, her mind was filled with the memory of another, identical set of flowers lying on the ground at her feet exactly one year before.

'Just don't expect me to stand around and watch'.

Aidan's last words reverberated inside her head, making her shake it hard in a vain attempt to drive them away. It was as if the year since she had heard them had never happened.

Aidan wouldn't come back. She'd known that to be the truth in the moment that she had looked into his face and seen the unyielding cold steel of rejection etched into every line, darkening his eyes to obsidian.

Aidan Wolfe was a proud, ruthless man. He was someone who lived life by his own rules and ignored the restrictions of a more conventional approach. He had pulled himself up by his own bootstraps, coming from nothing to become the head of a multi-faceted corporation that he was now. He had a reputation for being as tough as they came, someone who didn't suffer fools gladly and who gave no

16

quarter at all in his business dealings. But she would have sworn that with her he could have been so very different.

But, when it came down to it, how well had she known him? How well could you know anyone you had met barely six weeks before your wedding day? Even as Julia faced the truth of that question, Jane's words on the night of the fateful party came back to haunt her.

'Oh, God, Indy, no!' her friend had said, all the light and laughter dying from her face as she'd looked across the room in response to India's stunned declaration that the man of her dreams had just walked through the door. 'Not the Lone Wolfe himself! No one tangles with him and lives to tell the tale.'

'Why's that?' India had asked, her mind only half on the question, her eyes devouring the dark, saturnine features and tall, powerful body of the man who had caught her attention. 'Is he some sort of a heart-breaker?'

'Soul-breaker's more like it.' Her friend had shivered dramatically. 'Business negotiations or women, he treats them both the same. He takes what he wants and discards the rest without his heart even missing a beat. In fact, it's been rumoured that he actually doesn't even possess the organ in question, let alone the feelings supposed to go with it. So, you have been warned.'

But she hadn't cared, India admitted to herself. She hadn't cared who or what he was, or whether he was rich or poor, a success or failure. She had never believed in love at first sight before, but now she knew that she had been knocked completely off balance, her sense of reality rocked in a way that she had never experienced in her life.

And so she had made her way over to where Aidan stood, dark and devastating in black shirt and trousers topped by a loose black linen jacket, and, with uncharacteristic forwardness, had introduced herself to him.

'You may not know this,' she had said, her voice sliding up and down in a mixture of excitement and near-hysteria, 'but I'm the girl you've been waiting for all your life.'

'Are you, indeed?' Aidan had drawled, one dark eyebrow drifting upwards in intrigued speculation as he'd subjected her to a slow, deliberate scrutiny. Those deep brown eyes had scanned every inch of her from the top of her head, over the home-made dress and down to her slender feet, before he'd added, 'Do you know, you could be right?'

He had offered her a drink, and the rest was history. History that had turned so terribly sour in the end, leading as it had done to the farce of her wedding day. If only she had known...

But the truth was that she had never really known Aidan Wolfe—except perhaps in one way.

A tiny touch of colour crept into India's cheeks at the memory of the very physical, passionate nature of their relationship. Then faded again at the thought of the way that that very sensuality had been her undoing. It had rushed her into Aidan's bed and into that precipitous marriage, handing him the perfect weapon to turn against her.

Almost in the same moment that she had realised the depth of her love for him, that same love had been transformed into an equally powerful, deeply burning hatred.

That hatred had sustained her through the dark days that had followed. It had forced her out of bed on the mornings when all she'd wanted to do was to pull the covers over her head and hide away. It had given her the strength to ignore the speculative looks and whispered comments that had greeted her appearance in the village. If she gave in to the hurt, then Aidan had won. He would have succeeded in his cruel plan to humiliate her, and she would rather die than let that happen.

And so she had forced herself to get on with her life, meeting those curious glances with what she'd hoped was a confident smile, and holding her head high. The act had worked, seeming to convince people that she didn't care, and in the end she had almost come to believe it. Until today.

'When did these arrive?' she asked her brother, the catch

in her voice revealing feelings that went deeper than the careless gesture towards the flowers indicated.

'Coogan's delivered them at two this afternoon.'

Gary was clearly unaware of her struggle to impose some control over her emotions. But then, like most fourteen-year-olds, he lived in his own private world. He probably didn't even realise what day it was, the events of the previous year having faded from *his* mind at least.

'Did they say who they were from?'

And why two o'clock so precisely, unless they were from someone who knew the significance of that time? If the choice of flowers had already set her teeth on edge, now an uncomfortable suspicion ran like pins and needles along every nerve.

'Dunno. But there's a card somewhere if you want to look.'

She didn't; didn't want confirmation of her fears. But she just *had* to.

'Who's "A"?' Gary looked over her shoulder in curiosity. 'Some secret admirer?'

'Nothing like that.'

Did he really not know? Was it possible that he couldn't even guess? Or was it only in her own thoughts that the single, forceful initial could only ever mean one name?

The urge to tear the card into tiny pieces and fling them from her, with the bouquet following them, was almost overwhelming. Only the thought that such an emotional re-action was precisely what Aidan would have wanted stayed her hand.

Of course, deep down, she had known that it had to be Aidan who had sent the flowers. The cynical choice of blooms, deliberately matching the ones that had made up her wedding bouquet, and the delivery planned for the exact time of the aborted wedding service a year ago had left no room for hope that they could have been from anyone else. But, after all this time, how could he be so cruel, so vindictive? How he must hate her—and all over one rather silly, thoughtless declaration!

'I'll take these to the hospital tonight,' she said stiffly, knowing that to keep the bouquet in the house would be more than she could bear. 'Someone there will appreciate them.'

'But…' Gary looked bewildered, his frown one of confusion. 'They were meant for you—to wish you a happy…'

'They weren't meant to wish me a *happy* anything, Gary. And right now I've got too much on my plate to concern myself with the fact that today's my birthday.'

Wearily she ran a hand through her hair, raking the blue-black strands back from a face that strain had made pale and drawn.

'Mum's staying at the hospital again, so it'll just be you and me for supper tonight. But it'll have to be something out of the freezer, I'm afraid. I haven't got time to make anything from scratch before Jim comes to pick me up for another stint at Dad's bedside.'

'Is there any change?' Her brother's voice was sharp with anxiety. 'Any sign of Dad coming out of the coma?'

'None, I'm afraid, sweetie.'

The sight of Gary's troubled face, his teeth digging hard into his lower lip and his eyes suspiciously bright, had India moving to his side. Gently she put one hand on his arm, knowing from past experience that the small gesture was all the sympathy his spiky young masculinity could accept at the moment.

All thought of the hateful bouquet was pushed from her mind. Instead, her thoughts were filled by the memory of the scene she had just left in the hospital—the hushed atmosphere of the intensive care unit, the machines and tubes attached to her father's motionless body.

'But he is breathing on his own, at least—that's something. All we can do is wait.'

'But they've said that for days now!' Gary's voice was

rough with distress. His father's stroke had devastated him, and he had found it difficult to come to terms with events.

'I know, love.'

India's green eyes were dull and clouded. Like Gary, she found it almost impossible to accept that her father—who, at barely fifty, she had believed still in the prime of life— could have been felled so completely by the illness that had struck without warning just a week ago.

'But there's nothing else to do. He's in good hands, and all we can do is wait—and pray.'

Wait and pray. The words still echoed inside India's head some hours later when, feeling physically and mentally drained, she arrived back at the Grange after yet another trip to the hospital.

'Thanks for bringing me home, Jim.' She sighed, turning with a tired smile to the man at the wheel of the car. 'I don't think I'd have been up to driving myself, so I really appreciate it.'

'No trouble.' James Hawthorne smoothed a tidying hand over the light brown hair that the breeze from an open window had ruffled as he smiled back at her, blue eyes warm. 'You know I'm only too willing to help.'

India glanced towards the house, noting the darkened windows, the single light left burning in the hall.

'It looks like Gary's already gone to bed, so I hope you'll forgive me if I don't invite you in for coffee.'

'Nothing to forgive,' her companion returned easily as she pushed open her door. 'I wouldn't have accepted anyway. You look as if you need to get straight to bed.'

'Oh, I do!' India sighed. 'I feel as if I could sleep for a week. Some birthday, huh?'

'We'll make up for it when things get better,' James assured her. 'Now, you get off and get some rest. I'll see you tomorrow.'

India was halfway out of the car when an impulse had her turning back and pressing a spontaneous kiss on his left cheek.

'You've been so good to me. I don't know how to thank you.'

'No problem,' was the smiling response. 'You know I'd do anything for you. You only have to ask.'

From the look on his face it was plain that he wanted more than just the friendly kiss she had given him, and the realisation twisted her nerves sharply. Hastily she backed out of the car again, with rather more speed than grace.

'I'll see you tomorrow, then. Drive carefully, please.'

It wasn't Jim's fault that she couldn't feel anything for him, India reflected sadly as she watched his car move off down the drive and disappear into the darkness of the night. She doubted if she could feel anything for any man ever again. Aidan Wolfe had cured her of that foolishness.

'Oh, how sweet!'

'What…?'

A sharp cry of shock escaping her, India jumped like a startled cat as a voice sounded suddenly from the deep shadows cast by the house.

'"You've been so good to me".' The cynical tones echoed her words but gave them a dangerously different emphasis. '"I don't know how to thank you".'

After her initial panicked reaction, the sound of that terrifyingly familiar, husky intonation had India freezing in horror.

'I'm sure you'll find a way to thank him, won't you, Princess?'

And the use of that once familiar teasing nickname drove all hope of redemption from her head. One person had invented that name for her, playing on the fact that India had once been part of the British empire, and only one person had ever used it—affectionately at first. It was only later that she had been able to see the other, less complimentary undertones in it.

There was no hope now that she could be mistaken, she told herself, turning slowly with a sense of dreary resignation. At last she found that her tongue had loosened enough for her to croak, 'Hello, Aidan.'

He had been in her thoughts so much that if he had appeared as some unearthly apparition, conjured out of the air by her bleak memories earlier in the day, then she wouldn't have been surprised. But, of course, Aidan Wolfe was solid flesh and bone, six feet two of toned muscle over a powerful frame. There was nothing in the least ethereal about him.

His feet were planted firmly on the stone flags that lay before the heavy wooden main door, his hands resting loosely on lean hips, his head slightly to one side. His whole stance was one of mocking challenge as his dark eyes, eyes that were just pools of black in the shadowed planes of his face, met her stunned green ones in open provocation.

'What are you doing here?'

Aidan stepped forward into the light of the lamp that illuminated the courtyard. His smile was just a hateful, cruel curl of his lips that made her blood run cold.

'Would you believe I've come to wish you a happy birthday?'

'No.'

It was a clipped, curt rejection of his teasing question, and she made no attempt to respond to that mockery of a smile.

'And you know that I know that has to be the furthest thing from your thoughts.'

'Well, there you'd be wrong, you know,' Aidan put in with deceptive mildness, that smile growing wider. 'I do wish you a very happy—what? Twenty-fourth birthday? And a wonderful year to follow.'

He almost sounded as if he meant it, India told herself. But almost immediately she clamped down hard on that weak train of thought. Even to allow the possibility to slide into her mind was foolish in the extreme. Foolish and very dangerous.

'It can hardly be much worse than last year.'

She regretted the words as soon as they were out of her mouth, fearing that they gave away far too much. She didn't want this man to know of all the long, lonely nights she had spent lying awake in an agony of frustration, the dreary, empty days she had dragged herself through since he had abandoned her so brutally. Immediately she tried to cover her tracks.

'Though really I should thank you for what you did. You saved me from making what could quite possibly have been the worst mistake of my life.'

The way his head went back slightly, showing that her attack had hit home, made her give a small smile of satisfaction.

'But I'm sure you didn't come here to chat over old times.' Deliberately she laced the words with acid. 'So perhaps you'll tell me the real reason for your sudden materialisation.'

'Materialisation,' Aidan echoed in dark amusement. 'You make me sound like some alien being, or a ghost.'

Ghost indeed. The ghost of happier times, a reminder of the way she had once felt. India flinched away from the stab of anguish that pushed her into unconsidered speech.

'A werewolf or a vampire is more like it!' she flung at him.

'Now you're being fanciful.'

'Am I? Am I really?'

How she wished she could bring her voice down a note or two. It was too high, too shrill, too bitterly revealing. It infuriated her even more to remember that she had always promised herself that if she ever met this man again then she would be so cool, would freeze him out completely. She could never bear it if he knew just how badly he had hurt her.

'Well, let me tell you something, Mr Wolfe. In my mind, a vampire is just what you are! An emotional vampire, someone who preys on people's feelings, taking them and sucking them dry, then casting them aside without a second thought when you've tired of them.'

'Oh, come on.' The smooth voice mocked her outburst. 'You surely aren't claiming that I broke your heart? After all, it wasn't *me* you wanted but my money.'

His tone had sharpened noticeably on the last words, and now he took a couple of swift steps towards her, coming very close for the first time.

It took all India's self-control not to recoil in panic. She had forgotten just how tall he was, how broad his shoulders were under the immaculately white T-shirt and the loose linen jacket.

She had never seen Aidan quite so casually dressed before, she realised. In all the time that they had been dating he had stuck rigidly to the formal suits he wore for work as well as leisure. So now it was painfully disconcerting to feel her mouth dry in an instinctively sensual response to the way that the soft cotton clung to the honed lines of his chest, the denim jeans he wore with it emphasising the powerful length of his legs.

Oh, God, how could he still do this to her after all that had happened? She couldn't be so weak that he had only to appear and she fell straight back under his spell, could she?

'You broke my heart? Now who's being fanciful? We never had that sort of a relationship, and you know it. You wanted me and I wanted you.'

'And what I brought with me,' Aidan inserted brutally. 'So, tell me, how is it with your new lover?'

'Lover?' For a few seconds she couldn't focus her mind enough to think. 'Oh, Jim!'

'Yes, Jim.'

The twist to Aidan's mouth, the roughness of his voice, turned the name into an obscenity.

'"You've been so good to me" Jim. "I don't know how to thank you" Jim. What does he do for you, my lovely India? Does he give you more than I ever could? Was he the next wealthy man to walk through the door after I walked out of it?'

'Precisely! *You* walked out!' India pounced on the opening he had given her. 'You walked out on me, remember. So don't come the jilted fiancé—'

'I wouldn't dream of it,' Aidan responded coolly, stopping her dead. 'Believe me, he's welcome to you.'

Those dark eyes noted the way India clamped her mouth shut against any weak protest at the callousness, and his smile surfaced once more. The curl of his lips was even more predatory than before.

'But I wonder if he knows just how much it's going to cost him.'

'If you must know,' India declared, unable to endure his taunts any longer, 'Jim is just a very junior cog in the firm of Jenkins and Curran, my father's—'

'Your father's solicitors,' Aidan inserted dismissively. 'I know who they are only too well.'

'But how?'

'We've had dealings,' was the enigmatic response. 'Which reminds me. Where is your dear papa?'

The edge in his voice was worrying, an undertone of threat seeming to lurk in his words like jagged rocks underneath the still surface of a calm sea. Hearing it, India felt an intuitive shiver run down her spine, setting her protective instincts on red alert.

'Why do you want to know?' she asked warily.

'It was your father I came to see. Let's just say I have some important business to discuss with him.'

If she had felt apprehensive before, that cryptic remark made matters ten times worse. Even before her wedding day Aidan and her father had been at daggers drawn, and she very much doubted that time had done anything to ease the situation.

'I don't think he'd want anything to do with you!' The memory of the state in which she had just left her father sharpened her voice, giving it extra emphasis.

'Oh, he'll see me, darling. I promise you, he'll want to talk to me very much, and if he's wise he'll arrange a meeting very soon. So when will he be back?'

'And what is that supposed to mean?' India ignored the question, concentrating instead on the implications behind that 'if he's wise'.

'Just what it says,' Aidan returned indifferently. 'I want to see your father, and it would be better for him if I saw him soon. So when do you expect him home?'

'I don't know.'

Which at least was nothing more than the truth. No matter when her father came out of hospital, it would be a long time before he would be well enough to talk to anyone, let alone the predatory Lone Wolfe. But what possible business could connect two such disparate men?

'I could give him a message if you like,' she managed, her attempt at cool confidence sadly marred by the sudden realisation that Aidan was between her and the door.

If she wanted to get inside she would have to go past him, she told herself. The idea made her uneasy, uncomfortably aware of the heavy shadows cast by the trees, the silence of the night and the recollection of the fact that Gary's room was at the back of the house, well out of earshot.

'If you just tell me what you want to say.'

For a long moment Aidan considered. 'No.' He shook his dark head decisively. 'It's between the two of us. I'll find him later. Tell him I was looking for him.'

'Is that it?' India questioned, receiving another of those slanted, mocking glances that aggravated the already edgy way she was feeling.

'Were you looking for something more?'

'Not on your life!'

She was disconcerted to realise just how close he had come to her, suddenly only inches away from her.

'A pity.' It was a low, seductive murmur, one that drew her attention against her will. Drew it and held it as if she were hypnotised. 'Because I was just thinking that I couldn't let you go without a kiss for old times' sake.'

'For—!' India spluttered, a sense of panic gripping her round the throat, choking off her words as his head came even nearer, lowering to blot out the light of the moon.

He was so near that she could hear the sound of his breathing, catch the tang of some exclusive cologne. Her heart lurched into a wild, uneven rhythm that made her blood pound in her ears, and she was sure he must hear the accelerated beat of her heart.

'Don't you dare!'

Her voice was high and sharp, and it stilled that ominous movement, his head coming to a sudden halt.

'Don't you dare…'

It was less successful this time. A betraying quiver that she couldn't quite suppress deprived her words of the force she had aimed for.

A wicked smile curved his lips, revealing perfect white teeth.

'Oh, I dare,' he drawled softly. 'The question is, do you? You see, I wouldn't be content with just a peck on the cheek and a breathless thank-you such as you gave your so-kind Jim.'

'But you…'

'I what?' Aidan murmured when she struggled to find words to fling at him.

The trouble was that with that dark head so very close, with his lips curved into that deceptive softness, all she could think of was how it had once been. She could recall so vividly how it had felt to run her hands through the dark silk of his hair, to have that beautiful mouth against her own…

To her horror she found that she had actually raised her head, tilting it slightly, her lips parting as if to receive his kiss.

'I what, sweetheart?' Aidan repeated on a very different note, one so smokily sensual that it seemed to have the power to draw her soul from her body and straight into his ruthless hands. 'I rejected you, cast you off—is that it?'

She couldn't find any response. Her tongue seemed frozen and stiff inside her mouth.

'Ah, but you're forgetting one thing, my darling India. I may have walked away from the thought of tying myself down, but I could never refuse the invitation offered by that glorious body of yours. I was always unable to resist the temptation you offered, and, after twelve months, the hunger you arouse is stronger than ever.'

'Invitation!' India exploded, her head coming up sharply, green eyes blazing in rejection of his blunt declaration. 'Offer! I'm not inviting *anything*! And, believe me, I have nothing whatsoever to offer you ever again! If you think otherwise, then you have most definitely totally misread the signals.'

'Perhaps.' His tone implied that he very much doubted it. 'But, India, sweetheart—'

'And I am *not* your sweetheart, or anything else! How you can possibly even begin to imagine that after the way you treated me I would want anything at all to do with you, I just don't know. But...'

Drawing a deep breath, she snatched at the one thing she hoped would convince him once and for all.

'Get it through your thick skull that I am not available! As you saw, I'm with Jim now.'

Dear Jim. He wouldn't mind his name being taken in vain in this way. He would probably even enjoy the thought of being linked with her, in fantasy if not in reality. At least she could rely on him to back her up if her story was challenged.

'He's the only man in my life; the only one I want.'

If he argued, she thought, her breathing fast and uneven, if he so much as questioned her declaration or asked for proof she didn't know what she would do. That last outburst seemed to have used up all her remaining strength,

and she didn't feel she had anything in reserve with which
to fight him.

But Aidan's unexpected reaction seemed to blast apart
the last scrap of solid ground beneath her feet, destroying
the shreds of her composure as it did so.

'OK,' he said casually, shrugging those broad shoulders
in a gesture of supreme indifference. 'If that's how you
want it.'

It was how little he cared that really hurt. India found
herself frozen to the spot, unable to do anything more than
watch as he turned and strolled away, heading for the car
that was parked at the side of the house, almost invisible
in the shadows.

If he had ever felt anything for her, however little, then
surely he would have shown some reaction? Surely his face
would have betrayed a hint of disappointment, or anger, or
at the very least jealousy? Or was she being all sorts of a
fool even to hope?

But even the realisation that Aidan felt nothing at all
couldn't stop her heart from jolting painfully in her chest,
seeming to lurch almost into her throat, when he suddenly
paused and turned back to her.

'Tell your father I was here,' he said, and his voice had
returned to the ominously dark intonation that had so worried her earlier. 'And that we have important things to discuss.'

'What—?' India began, but her feeble attempt at speech
was brushed aside, falling to the ground like splintered
glass as it came up against the hard, unyielding mask of
his face.

'Just tell him I'll be back. And if he's wise he'll be here
to see me.'

In spite of the heat of the evening, the words sent a shiver
like the trail of icy water down India's spine. There could
be no mistaking the menace behind them—a threat made
all the worse by the fact that she had no idea what was
involved.

'But what…?'

But Aidan had gone. And as the dark, sleek car disappeared down the drive, turning the corner out of sight, she was suddenly swamped by a terrible sense of loneliness, a feeling of dread that was all the worse for having no rational explanation.

CHAPTER THREE

'I'LL be back.'

For two days now, Aidan's words had rung inside India's head, their disturbing undertones seeming to grow more and more ominous with each repetition. The fact that she could think of no reason at all for Aidan to want to speak to her father only added to her already deeply uneasy frame of mind.

There was no one she could share her anxiety with, either. Her mother was under enough strain as it was, spending each day and often all night at the hospital. She was usually too tense and anxious even to eat properly. And Gary was too young, already worried about his father.

I'll be back.

She didn't doubt that he meant it. Already she had found three messages from Aidan on her father's answering machine, the later ones distinctly less polite than the first. And only yesterday she had had a narrow escape when he had come to the door.

She had answered the summons of the bell automatically, but luckily had taken a second to glance out of an upstairs window before making her way down to the hall. The sight of the dark grey Jaguar parked in the driveway had had all the tiny hairs on the back of her neck lifting in instinctive alarm, freezing her to the spot.

A moment later Aidan's dark head and powerful shoulders had become visible below her as he'd moved restlessly, impatient for an answer. Instinct had had India shrinking back against the wall, hidden by a thick velvet curtain, just seconds before he'd looked up, dark eyes raking the upper windows with an intensity that had made her shiver.

It was as if he'd known she was there, had been able to sense her presence as the wolf scented its prey. Fearfully India had flattened herself against the wall, staying there until the roar of the car's engine told her he had gone. Even then, it had taken some minutes before she dared move at all.

But today at least the coast was clear, she acknowledged gratefully as she arrived back at the house with a load of groceries in the back of the car. There was no sign of anyone, no alien vehicle parked in the forecourt.

Relief made her heart lift, and she hummed softly to herself as she opened the boot and reached in for the two heavy shopping bags.

'Here, let me help you with those.'

'Oh, I...'

The bag she held almost slipped from her grasp, and she only avoided banging her head on the open end of the car by the narrowest of margins.

'Careful,' Aidan soothed, his voice and expression one of carefully assumed concern that she didn't believe in for a second. 'Let me take that.'

'I can manage perfectly well!'

Her thoughts were reeling in shock, sharpening her tone. It seemed almost as if he had been conjured up by her own mind.

'Where the hell did you spring from?'

'From Westbury,' Aidan responded, knowing very well that that was not what she had meant at all. 'I've been staying there for a few days.'

'But your car...?'

'Oh, I left that at the bottom of the drive and walked up.'

'I never saw it.'

Too late, she realised that she had given herself away.

Now Aidan would know that she had been looking for signs of his presence, worried that he might be around.

'I don't suppose you did.' His smile was slow and filled with a lazy mockery that told her he had caught her momentary lapse. The glint of dark amusement in his eyes brightened as he went on, 'But then, of course, I didn't exactly leave it in full view. You can't be too careful these days, with so many thieves and joy-riders around.'

And he knew very well that if she had seen his car she would have turned around at once and stayed well away until the coast was clear.

'And I didn't want you forewarned and so forearmed as you were when I called the other day.' Aidan confirmed her thoughts with such deadly accuracy that India's mouth actually fell open in shock.

'You knew?'

'Of course I knew. You forget, my dear India, that I know this house of old, and that I am very well aware of just which bedroom is yours.'

The sensual deepening of his tone, together with the smokiness of his eyes, had hot colour rising in her cheeks at the thought of just how he knew. The memory of those nights, just over a year ago, when—with her parents and Gary away on a visit to relatives—she had invited Aidan to stay at the Grange came back to haunt her. Of course he knew where her room—her bed—was. They had hardly moved out of it, except to fetch food, for the whole of that week.

'Now, let's get these inside.'

Taking advantage of the shock that had loosened her grip on the bag, Aidan eased it from her before she could protest. Then he hoisted the other one from the interior of the boot with a lack of effort that forced a reluctant and secret admission of envious admiration from her. She was well aware of just how heavy that bag was, but Aidan's one-handed ease made a nonsense of her own earlier struggle to get it into the car.

But then, of course, she was only too well aware of the strength of those sinewy, tightly muscled arms. She was also uncomfortably sensitive to the sensual impact of the way their impressive power was shown off to advantage by the short sleeves of the dark chocolate-coloured T-shirt he wore with oatmeal—coloured chinos.

The sun warmed the smoothly tanned skin, and her throat dried at the thought of the times she had felt those arms close around her in the throes of passion, holding her tight against the hard length of his body...

'India?'

A touch of amusement in the deep voice brought hot colour rushing into her face. She couldn't avoid the uncomfortable suspicion that Aidan had known just what thoughts had distracted her, the gleam in his eyes intensifying to a positively devilish light as his smile widened wickedly.

'If we don't get this food inside, some of the frozen stuff will start to defrost in this heat. And I want...'

'My father isn't at home!'

It was all she could think of to say. The idea of Aidan setting foot inside her home ever again sent such a shudder of revulsion down her spine that it was all she could do not to let him see it. As it was, she knew all the blood had drained from her face.

'Oh, I know,' Aidan returned easily. 'That's why I waited. But I have to admit to being surprised when you turned up. I expected you'd be at work all day.'

'I don't have a job.'

India's voice was tight. When she had first met him she had had a position as a secretary to a local businessman, a job she had been only too glad to give up as soon as she had become engaged.

In the year since her wedding day she had only been able to find temporary work. And lately, just when she needed it most, even that uncertain source of income had dried up. Irrationally, she felt deeply resentful—as if Aidan had been responsible for that misfortune too.

'Of course not.' Something in his tone stung sharply. 'So you're free all day.'

'Yes, but you—'

'I have all the time in the world,' Aidan put in, obviously anticipating India's next attempt at persuading him to leave. 'I'm on holiday.'

'I didn't know you took them,' India cut in sharply. 'I mean, you always were a workaholic when we were…'

'When we were together?' he completed smoothly when the realisation of just what she had been about to say froze her tongue. 'Well, I think you'll find that quite a few things have changed since then. Now, are you going to open this door or not?'

India devoutly wished that she could do no such thing. But Aidan's determined stance and the obdurate look in his eyes brought her up hard against the realisation that, unless she was prepared to indulge in an undignified and probably totally pointless struggle for her shopping, she would either have to do as he said or risk losing all their food for the coming week.

One look at those long, tanned fingers clamped firmly around the handles of the bags decided her on the side of discretion rather than valour. With a sigh of resignation she accepted defeat and opened the door.

'And besides, I didn't just come to see your father.'

'Well, don't try to claim that you wanted to renew our friendship,' India muttered ungraciously.

'Friendship?'

One dark eyebrow quirked up in frank scepticism, and his voice held an undertone that she was beyond interpreting.

'Don't you think that's something of an understatement for what we had?'

'What we *had* was a lie from start to finish, and it's over now, gone for good. Dead and buried.'

'Is that a fact?'

'It's the only fact that I know!' The only one she would ever admit to him, anyway.

All trace of his mocking humour seemed to have evaporated, leaving his face cold and distant, set into harshly brutal lines.

'You're surely not claiming that I broke your heart? That I did anything more than cause you some social embarrassment, and perhaps lower your expectations of the future a little?'

'Broke my heart?' India repeated, the need for control, to ensure that not even the tiniest suggestion of the truth seeped past her defences, making her tone coldly brittle. 'No, I'm not claiming that at all.'

If she was to convince him of that fact, she had to do it once and for all.

'In fact, as I said the other night, I really should be grateful to you. If you hadn't walked out on me like that, I'd have been trapped in a very unwise and totally unsuitable marriage. Before very long—possibly even by now—we would both have realised our mistake, but would have had to go through the unpleasantness of a divorce in order to get out of it.'

'Instead of which you find yourself free and available, and perfectly positioned to marry your darling Jim.'

As on the previous occasion, the total lack of any feeling in Aidan's response brought a flaring pain so violent that she had to bite down hard on her lower lip.

All she could think of was the need to make sure there was no possibility he could doubt her sincerity, and so she pounced on the opening he had offered her. If he wanted to believe she and Jim were a couple, then who was she to stop him?

'That's right. Jim has—kept me company…'

She had been about to say 'comforted me', but caught herself just in time.

'Ever since last year. We've become very close, and I think our families are expecting an announcement soon.'

'My congratulations,' Aidan drawled. 'I'm sure you'll be well suited.'

He made the possibility sound like a life sentence rather than a prospect for happiness.

'Obviously a trainee solicitor is considered a better bet by your father than someone with my background.'

'Well, Jim's uncle is an MP, and his grandmother was an earl's daughter,' India told him with a terrible sense of hammering nails into an already well-sealed coffin.

'That'd just about do it,' Aidan growled. 'Shall I put this stuff away?'

'There's no need.'

It was almost impossible to match the carelessness of his tone with her own, to hide the stab of bitterness his indifference brought.

'But thanks for carrying them in.'

Automatically she looked towards the door, anticipating that he would take the hint and leave. But Aidan simply shook his head with a calmness that set her teeth on edge.

'Oh, no, my lovely. I'm not leaving until I've had words with your fool of a father.'

To India's horror, he calmly deposited one of the bags on the table and began to unpack it systematically, putting the various tins and packages in their places with a familiarity that struck at her heart with its bitter memories.

'You can't. He's...out.'

If she had had any hope that her father's illness might make Aidan hold back, show a little consideration, she would have told him the truth. But this man and Bruce Marchant had always been at daggers drawn. She wouldn't put it past Aidan to march straight round to the hospital to confront his opponent about whatever matter was on his mind. And, already uneasy about his motives, she quailed inside at the thought of what the result of such a meeting would be on her father's already frail health.

'Obviously. So when will he be back?'

'I can't say.'

'Can't or won't, Princess?'

'I don't *know* when he'll be back!'

'Then I'll wait until he returns. He can't stay away all day.'

'Yes, he can!' Belated inspiration had struck. 'He's gone away for the weekend, and…' India's voice faded as Aidan shook his head reprovingly.

'Nice try, sweetheart, but too late. If you wanted to convince me, you should have come up with that one much earlier. And besides, I saw his car in the garage. Wherever he's gone it isn't far.'

He didn't miss a trick, India thought despairingly. Those keen dark eyes observed every little thing about his surroundings, and the shrewd brain that had made his fortune considered the information, assessing the situation and coming to a swift conclusion. She was beginning to feel like some particularly interesting scientific specimen under observation in a controlled laboratory experiment.

'Think what you like.' Her tone acknowledged defeat. 'But *don't* call me sweetheart! I am not your anything, and never will be again!'

'Well, I have to admit that it isn't exactly apposite,' Aidan flung back, putting the last tin in a cupboard and folding the carrier bag with firm, precise movements. 'You've been anything but sweet ever since I arrived.'

'What did you expect?' India exploded, unable to believe the gall of the man. 'After the way you treated me, I'd hardly be likely to throw myself into your arms and kiss you senseless!'

'I recall many occasions on which you did just that.' There was a predatory gleam in the depths of those eyes now. 'And I remember them as being very enjoyable, for both of us. All the more so because they usually led to—'

'Well, memories are all you're going to have!' India broke in sharply, knowing only too well just what those occasions had led to.

Neither did she need any reminder of how those passionate encounters had felt. Simply thinking of them had raised her pulse rate to racing point, making her breathing unnaturally rapid and rawly uneven.

In the past, a simple kiss of greeting from this man had had the effect of a lighted match laid to a tinder-dry bonfire, making desire flare between them, roaring out of control in seconds.

'That's all right by me—for now.'

Aidan's smile was one that might have been on the face of a hunting tiger as it lay in the sun, lazily watching its prey, knowing that when the time was right it would spring. But right now he couldn't be bothered, that smile said, and his voice was a sensually indolent purr, threaded through with a dark line of threat.

'But I have a *very* good memory. A cup of coffee would be nice,' he added pointedly, startling India with his abrupt change of mood.

'Don't you have anything better to do?'

'Frankly, no.'

The blunt declaration left no room for argument, and India could only shrug her shoulders resignedly as she moved to fill the kettle.

'Why do you want to see my father anyway?' She tried to make it sound casual, even if it was the furthest thing from the way she was feeling.

'He owes me money.'

You and a hundred others. India barely bit back the despondent comment in time, but Aidan had caught something of her change in expression.

'You don't seem surprised.'

'I'm not.'

If there was one thing that made her father's illness even more difficult to bear, it was the discovery of the mountain of debts he had run up, unknown to anyone else.

It seemed that no sooner had the ambulance taken him to hospital than all sorts of demanding creditors had crawled out of the woodwork. There had also been letters from the bank, demanding that Bruce Marchant paid off some of his excessively large overdraft, not to mention the instalments on a loan he had taken out and on which he was behind with payment.

'I'm just surprised that he borrowed anything from *you*.'

The last word was emphasised by the way that she slammed the mug of coffee down onto the table in front of him.

'Tainted money, hmm?' Aidan murmured cynically. 'Not quite the sort of thing that blue-bloods like you want to soil their hands with.'

'Oh, now you're being ridiculous! That wasn't the only thing that worried my father. He was concerned by the stories of your wild youth, run-ins with the police.'

'The reports in the papers were exaggerated. I admit I was no saint—but then, is anyone when they're an adolescent?'

'You haven't been a teenager for over fifteen years! Or are you claiming that the men and women—particularly the women—you've used and discarded on your way to the top are just a figment of the tabloids' imagination too?'

'And are you claiming that your parents—your father at least—never believed that their sort of inherited wealth was far superior to money earned by hard work?'

He hadn't answered the question, India realised. But then, did he really have to? Was she really fool enough to think he might actually *care* about the beauties with whom his name had been linked, usually so briefly, in the past?

'In our case, "wealth" is a far from accurate term! For as long as I can remember, and certainly since my grandfather's death embroiled us in the problems of death duties, we've existed in a form of genteel poverty where appearance barely papered over the cracks. If you'd looked underneath, you'd have seen there was nothing of any substance...'

'Which is where I came in.'

'You know I never shared my father's opinions on—'

'No—*you* didn't care where the money came from, so long as there was plenty of it and it took you out of that ''genteel poverty'' you so hated,' Aidan inserted in a voice that seemed to freeze the air around them, making it difficult to breathe.

Suddenly it was as if she had slipped back in time, seeing herself little more than a year ago at that party that had started it all.

If it hadn't been for Rob, she wouldn't have felt that way in the first place. Rob—the man she had been seeing for the past few months, and with whom she had believed herself more than halfway in love. She had been so convinced of her feelings that only the week before the party she had finally given in to his persistent pressure and slept with him—her own first experience of physical lovemaking.

If the experience hadn't been everything she had hoped for, and certainly not all that the books she had read had led her to expect, she had told herself that it was only the result of inexperience. Time and commitment could only make things better—or so she'd believed.

And so she had been devastated when only a day or so later Rob had brusquely, and with brutal indifference to her feelings, broken off the relationship.

In an attempt to drown her sorrows, India had downed a couple of glasses of wine with more haste than she was used to. Her feelings of hurt pride and loss had been made even worse by the appearance of Rob himself at the party, with another woman on his arm.

'His boss's daughter, no less!' she complained to her friends, hiding her hurt behind a veil of contempt as she went on, 'But I mean—just look at her! That hair isn't natural for a start. And, well, to call her a bimbo would be an insult to all self-respecting airheads. What on earth can he see in her?'

'Face it,' Rose said, her tone one of knowing cynicism, 'What he really sees when he looks at Miss Bannister is a private income of X thousand a year and an easy way into

Daddy's good books—not to mention, if he plays his cards right, the prospect of a *very* comfortable future. Your family may have a high society name, Indy, and the family tree to go with it—but you haven't got the disposable *income* men like Rob look for.'

'And what income the Marchants do have is taken up by that crumbling old pile my father insists on calling the ancestral home!' India agreed. 'It's going to need a new roof soon, and there's not enough in the bank to fund it.'

'Not a problem dear Miss Bannister is likely to have to concern herself with,' Jane put in with a nod towards the dance floor, where the blonde was draped all over Rob. 'That little slip of nothing she's wearing is fresh from the Paris catwalks, and I'll bet that what Daddy paid for it would go a long way towards your new roof. Our high street couture just can't compete.'

'High street!' India's laugh was wry. 'You must be joking. I made this myself, from one of Mum's old evening dresses, cut down and restyled.'

Another glance towards Rob and his attentive companion twisted the knife deep inside her heart.

'Oh, God, I'm sick and tired of genteel poverty! I think it's high time I did something about it. You just watch me! I'm going to find myself a wealthy husband, one who can keep me in the manner to which I have every intention of becoming accustomed. Then I can just sit back and enjoy myself, not have to worry about anything.'

'Well, you couldn't do better than to start here, tonight,' her friend had told her. 'There must be the cream of the society, artistic and business worlds right here under one roof. You could take your pick.'

'I intend to!'

Buoyed up by the wine, India hadn't cared if her voice carried.

'And I don't plan on waiting for him to come to me. In fact, the very next rich man who walks through that door will find himself on the receiving end of such a campaign of seduction and enticement that he won't be able to resist me. I'll bet you anything you like that I'll have his ring on my finger before he knows what's hit him—three months at most, start to finish!'

'That was how you saw it, wasn't it?' Aidan's cold voice broke into her memories now. 'Correct me if I'm wrong.'

'I don't suppose you'd believe me if I said it was all a joke?' she managed, not meeting his eyes.

'In that case, the joke was on you,' Aidan returned harshly, his steely eyes and the tightness of the muscles in his face driving home the message of his tone.

'I didn't know you were listening.'

'No?' Aidan laughed nastily. 'You really slipped up there, didn't you, darling? You must have thought you were home and dry. As ordered, one extremely wealthy man who seemed to fall straight into your carefully baited trap.'

That laugh was worse the second time around, a grim travesty of humour that made India wince away in distress.

'What a pity that you hadn't realised that the window behind you was open when you hatched your grasping little plot, and that it carried every word of your conversation out to where I had just arrived at the front door. As they say, forewarned is forearmed. You should have seen your face. You looked as if all your Christmases had come at once and you'd got exactly what you asked Santa for.'

'Well, you got what you wanted too!'

Unable to bear his goading any longer, India needed to lash out at him, verbally at least, make him feel a little of her inner distress. The fact that her own conscience wasn't exactly comfortable with the events he was making her remember only made matters worse.

'And what was that?'

His voice was freezing again, and India shivered in nervous response

'You got *me*! You wanted my body—you made that only too plain. You wanted me in your bed, nothing more, nothing less, so you went along with my "grasping little plot" because it suited you. Or are you going to try and deny that now?'

Aidan's emphatic, silent shake of his head, the dark eyes fixed disturbingly on her face, drove that jagged knife in a few inches deeper, twisting it viciously in the wound.

'So you wanted sex. You wanted to screw me...'

She didn't care how crude she sounded, how harsh and vicious her tone had become. Her emotions felt crude. She felt soiled, dirty, used and discarded.

'And, boy, did you do that! You took what you wanted for as long as you wanted, promising marriage and happy ever after just to keep me sweet! But then, when you'd had enough, when you grew tired...'

'Damn you!'

India's voice failed her suddenly, the words disintegrating in her throat as Aidan flung the savage imprecation at her, getting to his feet in a violent movement, his chair scraping back over the floor with a harsh, ugly sound.

'Damn you to hell, Princess! If it's truth time, then it's that for both of us,' he declared, coming round the table towards her, his face set in an expression that had her shrinking away fearfully, reading danger in his look.

But Aidan's hands came out swiftly, fastening onto her arms, hard fingers digging painfully into soft flesh as he easily controlled her impulse to escape. Unable to move, she could only turn her head away—anything to avoid looking into his eyes.

'And you'll listen,' he growled into her stubbornly averted face. 'You'll hear what I have to say if I have to shake every damned word into you.'

Suiting action to the words, he gave her a rough shake. Not violent, but controlled just enough to let her know what it would be like if his temper finally broke free from the constraint he was imposing on it.

'*Yes*, I wanted you—'

'For sex,' India couldn't stop herself from inserting, and

out of the corner of her eye saw the hard nod of his head
that confirmed her words.

'I've never denied that. I'd be a fool to try. I've only got
to look at you to want you—and even the knowledge that
you're nothing but a cheap, money-grabbing little blood-
sucker isn't enough to change the way I feel, unfortunately.
I wish it was. But you got one thing wrong.'

'No…'

The protest escaped involuntarily, India's head going
back in shock as her mind focused on and fully registered
just what he had said. *I've only got to look at you to want
you.* Present tense—not past.

'No!' She didn't want him to say it, didn't want to hear
her fears confirmed.

'*Yes.*'

His smile was hateful, curling his lips in acknowledge-
ment of the way that the sudden darkening of her eyes told
him she had guessed what was coming.

'Oh, yes, my darling Princess. You got one thing totally
and unequivocally wrong, and that one thing makes all the
difference. You can say that I got what I wanted and, in a
way, I did. But I didn't get *enough* of it—nowhere near
enough.'

Hopelessly, desperately, India shook her head, her hands
coming up before her face as if she could actually ward off
what he was saying. But Aidan ignored her and ploughed
on ruthlessly.

'I never grew tired of you—not in that way at least. I
wanted you in my bed then, wanted you with a need so
sharp it hurts just to *think* of it, and I want you now. In
fact, I want you more than ever, and nothing that's happened has done anything to change that.'

CHAPTER FOUR

'I DIDN'T get enough—nowhere near enough.'

Aidan's harsh-voiced declaration swung round and round in India's head, gaining further devastating impact with each repetition. It almost seemed as if a grenade had just exploded right in her face, blasting her thought processes to bits.

The only thing she could see was Aidan's eyes, ebony-dark, no light in them at all, holding her stunned gaze with a powerfully mesmeric force.

'I never got enough of you,' he conferred, dropping his voice even lower, so that it seemed to coil round her beleaguered senses like thick, warm smoke. 'Not then, my lovely, and certainly not now.'

Inwardly, India shivered at the huskily sensual promise in his voice. Or did she mean threat? Right now, she neither knew nor cared. But then a new thought struck with stunning force, making her pull herself up sharply.

This was exactly what he wanted, she realised. He had set out deliberately to throw her off balance, and she had responded exactly as he had planned. If she showed fear or reacted nervously then he had won, or at least gained a very powerful advantage—and she was damned if she was going to let him get away with that!

Swallowing hard, she moistened dry lips with her tongue, and when she saw his dark-eyed gaze drop down to follow the tiny movement she deliberately made herself repeat it, more slowly this time. The change in pace turned the gesture into a lazily lascivious self-caress, like the sensuous reaction of a cat that had just cleared a saucer of cream, and she knew its impact wasn't lost on the man before her.

'So you still want me,' she murmured huskily. 'That doesn't surprise me. After all, we always were good together.'

She had caught *him* off balance now; she knew that from his sudden stillness, the way he blinked hard, just once. This made the odds a little more even, she thought, unable to suppress the tiny smile of triumph that curled her lips up at the corners.

Looking him straight in the eyes, her face alight with teasing challenge, she let that smile grow very slowly.

'After all, you don't have to like someone in order to fancy them.'

'You certainly don't,' Aidan breathed on a raw note. 'And if you want proof...'

Before India could begin to think, to guess what he had in mind, he had swung her round to face him fully, gathering her up into his powerful arms, dragging her hard against the unyielding wall of his chest as his dark head came down and his mouth took hers in a harsh, almost brutal kiss.

'After all,' he growled against her mouth, 'what has liking got to do with this?'

It was the response she had expected, the one she had been aiming for, and those few seconds of mental preparation enabled her to meet the demand of his kiss with a confidence that surprised even herself. She even kissed him back, letting her mouth soften and running the tip of her tongue over the hard lips that crushed hers, smiling in triumph as she heard his groan of response.

Two could play at this game, she told herself, letting her body relax against his, even allowing herself to give a sensually provocative little wriggle that brought her into more intimate contact with his lean, hard frame.

But that was where things started to go shockingly, worryingly wrong.

India had started out on this in a mood of almost playful challenge. She had expected something rather like a formal fencing match, the stylised, almost light-hearted thrust and parry, advance and retreat of two closely matched opponents. She had known there would be sparks, but had thought that the emotional swords they used would stop either of them from scoring any direct hits—at least, not ones that hurt.

But there was nothing in the least light-hearted in Aidan's approach, or, for that matter, in her response. In the space of a couple of heartbeats the mood changed from cool, through smouldering to a blazing heat that made her blood pound in her veins. Her head was swimming, her heart racing in a wild, pagan rhythm.

She was no longer teasing but deadly, dangerously serious. Her kisses met Aidan's demand for demand, her moans of response echoing his choked cries. The need to feel warm skin against skin was suddenly so overwhelming that her hands tugged at his T-shirt, pulling the loose top free from the leather belt at his waist.

'So you haven't forgotten what it was like.' His laugh was husky, half humour, half desperation.

Forgotten, India thought hazily. Never!

She might have believed that she had pushed these sensations from her mind, but they had only been locked away in some temporary hiding place where she didn't dare look at them. And now Aidan had turned the key that freed all the whirling emotions, the yearning need, to torment her once more. She felt as if lightning had scored a direct hit to her heart, sending blazing electricity shooting through her veins. The heat that built up moved lower and lower until it centred at the innermost core of her body. Aching need made her crush herself hard against Aidan's hips, feeling the unmistakable evidence of his answering desire in the heated hardness there.

'Oh, India, this was what was always there between us. This is what never went wrong.'

The buttons on her top were wrenched from their fastenings, exposing the warm curves of her breasts in the fine, lacy bra. A second later a choking cry of delight escaped her at the devastating sensation of his hot mouth on her delicate skin, pressing greedy, demanding kisses along the soft contours and down, down...

When his lips closed over one proud nipple, tugging softly, her response was one of such delicious agony that it was impossible to separate it from the burning shaft of desire that seared through every cell.

'More?' Aidan's voice was thick and rough.

'More!'

Her echoing sigh was the only answer of which she was capable. She was unable to drag her mind away from the sensations his caresses were sparking off, the electric shocks of pure excitement that made her skin quiver beneath his touch so that it was impossible to form any more coherent response.

The pressure of his hard strength against her body had bent her backwards, her hips coming into contact with the huge, scrubbed pine kitchen table so that now she was half lying along its length. The hard wood supported her back as her hands clenched over the soft collar of his T-shirt, pushing it up and aside so that she could touch the heated satin of his skin.

A low murmur of delight escaped her as she saw the strong muscles clench convulsively under the caress of her fingertips.

'God, Princess,' he choked. 'If you knew...'

The hoarse-voiced words were shut off with shocking abruptness. Aidan's whole body stilled suddenly, his dark head lifting sharply.

'Aidan?'

Still in the grip of the heated delirium that had possessed her body, India had murmured the petulant protest thoughtlessly, her body rebelling against the sudden cessation of the delight it had been experiencing. But the next moment something about the quality of his stillness, the realisation that he was listening intently, froze her tongue and had her straining to hear what sound had alerted him.

'Indy! Hi, I'm back!' Her brother's voice reached her from the hall.

'Oh, my God! Gary!'

Panic giving her a strength she hadn't known she possessed, she pushed at Aidan's large form, knowing a huge sense of relief at the realisation that he was already levering himself upwards. One strong hand fastened round her wrist, pulling her upright with him, the other going to smooth the disordered T-shirt down over his exposed torso.

'Indy? Where are you?'

'Here.' Her voice quavered weakly, her hands shaking as she tried to adjust her own clothing and failed miserably. 'In the kitchen.'

She would never be ready in time, she thought frantically as his footsteps sounded in the hall. Her fingers refused to obey her, turning into clumsy thumbs as she fumbled with her buttons. She swore in frustrated desperation.

She stilled in shock as, having cast an assessing glance in her direction, Aidan moved suddenly. Cool hands closed over hers, calmly removing them from her blouse, and a moment later the buttons had all been fastened with swift efficiency.

Still without a word, he reached for a hairbrush that lay on the nearby Welsh dresser, waiting only to be sure that she was capable of using it before he raked both hands through his own ruffled dark locks to smooth them. He had just taken a couple of diplomatic steps away from her side when the door opened.

'I've got news, Sis! Great news!'

Her brother was so excited that he probably wouldn't even have noticed if she and Aidan had remained in their earlier compromising positions, India told herself wryly. In fact, she doubted if he would have been bothered if they had been even more intimately entwined.

Which they might have been, she realised on a wave of

shock. If her brother had arrived a few moments later, or Aidan hadn't been quite so alert, things might have been very different.

She hadn't even heard the front door open. She had been too far gone in desire, too absorbed by this man's kisses and caresses to be aware of anything but him. That thought was so devastating that it drove her mind away from what Gary was saying, the recollection of just where he had come from occurring to her too belatedly to stop him.

'When I was at the hospital Dad opened his eyes! It was just for a moment, but he did it! The doctors say—'

'Gary!' Recovering some degree of control, India interrupted hastily. 'We have a visitor.'

Her nod directed his attention to Aidan, now seated at the table and sipping at his coffee, looking for all the world as if he hadn't moved from that position in the past hour or more.

'Oh—hi, Aidan.'

Gary's casual acceptance of the older man's presence stunned his sister. But then, being affected by a strong dose of hero-worship where Aidan was concerned, her brother had never joined in the general condemnation of his behaviour at the wedding.

'Hello, yourself,' Aidan returned equally casually. But India had caught the faint frown between his dark brows, the narrowing of those deepset eyes, and knew that behind the deceptively relaxed exterior his calculating mind was working overtime.

She was right.

'Your father, you said,' Aidan commented softly. 'Why is he in hospital?'

'Don't you know? Didn't Indy tell you about his stroke?'

'She obviously hadn't got round to it yet.'

Aidan's deliberate drawl echoed the sardonic gleam India knew must be in his eyes. She had heard that dark-edged tone many times before, and so knew the expression that went with it.

'I think—' she began through gritted teeth, but he didn't
let her finish.

'*I* think you'd better let Gary tell me,' he put in, in a
tone that made it plain she would be all sorts of a fool to
argue.

To protest any further would only make matters worse,
she knew, closing her mouth hard against the furious outburst that threatened to escape her. She had no option but
to keep quiet.

'So, what about your father?' Aidan knew he had her
beaten.

While Gary related the story of their father's illness India
pushed herself into action, forcing herself to refill the kettle
and make fresh coffee. Not because she wanted any, and
certainly not because she felt in any way hospitably inclined towards Aidan, but simply for something to do.

She needed some sort of physical action to distract herself from the disturbingly uncomfortable sensitivity that
still lingered all over her body like some gnawing ache.
Every nerve seemed to be stretched tight in anticipation of
the fulfilment that it had yearned for and had been so
abruptly denied. The building excitement had been doused
so swiftly and so violently that it had been as if a door had
slammed painfully right in her face.

She tried to convince herself that if she didn't look at
Aidan then this unpleasant feeling might fade, that her over-
wrought senses might return to some degree of comfort at
least. But in this she was bitterly disappointed. It seemed
that, where he was concerned, her personal radar was on
full alert, so that she could feel his presence as intently as
if he were actually still pressed up close against her.

She could almost hear that clever, incisive brain ticking
over, absorbing the facts Gary was giving him and working
out just how he could turn them to his advantage. Because
he would want to use them in that way; she had no doubt
about that.

So it was with a sense of total disbelief that, as Gary

finished his story, she heard Aidan say quite matter-of-factly, 'Well, I rather suspected something like this might happen. It's all rather a mess, isn't it? But we can get it sorted out.'

That had India slamming down her mug and swinging round with a speed that betrayed her feelings.

'We?' she questioned sharply, her already uneasy state of mind aggravated by the dazzling smile he turned in her direction.

'Well, clearly you need help. I'm prepared to do anything I can…'

'No, thank you!' She'd rather die. 'We're managing fine.'

'Seems like it.' His scorn was open now. 'It's been obvious from the moment I arrived that you have more than enough on your mind, and anyone with eyes to see has to be aware of the fact that the house and its grounds have been badly neglected of late. You admitted yourself that there are financial problems.'

'Gary…'

Alerted by her brother's sudden lift of his head, the frankly curious glance he turned in her direction, India reacted swiftly to practise as much damage limitation as possible.

'I need to get the washing done. You promised you'd strip the beds for me.'

'Oh, but Indy—'

'Scoot, kid.' Unexpectedly, Aidan took India's side. 'I'll still be here when you've got the job done.'

Not if I can help it, India vowed. And as soon as the door had closed behind her brother she rounded on Aidan, green eyes blazing defiance.

'Your offer of help is appreciated.'

She had to force herself to say it. She had resolved to be strictly polite, refusing to lower herself to snapping at him—though her tone made it plain that appreciation was very far from the way she was really feeling.

'But, really, we don't need it, so—'

'It wasn't an *offer*, Princess,' Aidan put in with a smile that sent shivers down her spine. 'Offers give you the chance to consider, to accept or refuse—this one isn't up for debate. I came here to see your father, and he obviously isn't well enough to talk to me, so I'll stick around until he is.'

'So your suggestion of *help* was only a smokescreen to put Gary off the track! What you really mean is that Dad owes you money and you're not going back without it!'

Her heart jumped painfully as Aidan got to his feet once more, crossing the kitchen to wash out his mug under the tap. The movement reminded her forcefully of just how big and imposing a man he was, his height and breadth seeming to dominate the sunlit room.

'Just how much does Dad owe you, anyway?'

'A lot,' Aidan returned with laconic brutality.

India dug her teeth into her lower lip to hold back the groan that almost escaped her. She should have known! Each new bill, every new demand, had revealed more and more of the financial mess that her father had got himself into. It was as if the letters were spades, digging a deeper and deeper pit until there would be no hope of getting out.

'Precisely how much is "a lot"?'

Perhaps she could pay *this* bill. She'd do anything to get Aidan off her back, out of her home and her life again.

Aidan took his time about replying, deliberately dragging the moment out by drying the mug and replacing it on the appropriate shelf.

Once again his knowledge of the kitchen stabbed at India's heart. In spite of her struggle to control them, her wilful thoughts persisted in superimposing another image on top of his tall, muscular form.

In her mind's eye she could see him as he had been a year before, during that wildly erotic week they had spent together. That broad chest had been tanned and shirtless, the feet bare, his only clothing the navy boxer shorts he had pulled on after leaving her bed. Whistling tunelessly, he had been piling a wonderful assortment of food onto plates for them to take back upstairs and feed to each other in the brief space of time before desire took possession of them once more.

'Thinking of buying me off, darling?' Aidan's sardonic tone wrenched her out of her memories. 'I doubt if you could ever find enough to clear this bill, even if you were considering a sort of payment in kind.'

His eyes dropped deliberately to the scrubbed top of the pine table.

'You couldn't! You wouldn't!'

'Try me.' It was low—voiced, suspiciously soft, almost gentle—but there was no mistaking the blunt challenge in his eyes.

'You think I'd sell my soul...'

Aidan's grim smile stopped her in mid-sentence.

'I don't think it's *souls* we're talking about here. After all, you weren't so very concerned with matters spiritual a year ago. You were only too willing to sell yourself for the price of a wedding ring then.'

'It wasn't like that!'

'So what was it like? We've already ascertained that to you marriage meant a comfortable future, financial security for life...'

At the time it had meant so very much more, but she didn't dare let him know that now. For one thing, she was sure that *this* Aidan, this cold, calculating man who had his own private reasons for hunting down her father in this way, would never believe her. For another, she could no longer connect with those past feelings any more.

'While I got precisely what I wanted—you in my bed.'

'You mean, you used me until you tired of me.'

'Used?'

One black eyebrow winged upwards questioningly, and once more those dark eyes rested thoughtfully on the table-top.

Disbelievingly India saw that the smile that played around his shapely mouth was surprisingly warm, and almost gently reminiscent. It totally transformed his face— until she looked into his eyes and saw the total lack of warmth there, the cold hardness of their deeply shadowed colour.

'Perhaps we were both using each other. But there's one thing you've got completely wrong, you know, my darling.'

'And what's that?'

India spoke through teeth gritted against the obvious insincerity of that 'my darling'. Only a few moments ago she had differentiated this Aidan and the one she had known in the past, but she couldn't have been more wrong.

The real truth was that she had never really known him in any way whatsoever. She had only seen what he had let her see, what she had wanted to see. Naively, crazily, blinded by the way she had felt then, she had convinced herself that he felt that way too.

'You're no fool, Princess, and neither are you blind.'

Leaning towards her, Aidan looked deep into her widened eyes, holding her transfixed with the dark intensity of his gaze.

'You know you're lovely—spectacular. You're a gorgeous, sexy woman, the most beautiful female I have ever seen in my life.'

India had always loved the sound of Aidan's voice. Deep and husky, it could sound as if it was murmuring sensual words of love even if he was simply reciting the alphabet. And now, expressing such extravagant compliments, it was irresistible.

She couldn't let him go on; had to speak in order to break free from the sensual spell he was weaving around her. But her tongue wouldn't form any words as Aidan smiled devastatingly.

'You know I never tired of you. I only had to look at you to feel hot as hell. I still do.'

It was as if a fire had been lit somewhere beneath India's

feet. The heat of it seemed to be licking at her body, warming the blood in her veins, so that it pulsed upwards, flooding the rest of her.

Already her arms and legs were glowing as a result, and the skin on her upper body was so sensitive that even the soft cotton of her blouse was an agony of abrasive friction against the tender cells of her flesh. Her breasts felt swollen and tight, and forceful waves ebbed and flowed along every nerve, threatening to betray her by staining her face with a wanton, rising colour.

'And you feel the same; I know you do.'

Reaching out, Aidan brushed the knuckles of one hand softly down her cheek, his smile growing as he saw her swiftly indrawn breath.

'You proved it just now. Which is why the next few weeks of sharing the same house should prove very interesting.'

It took perhaps the space of two heartbeats for what he had said to sink in, but when it did the effect was like a bolt of lightning striking straight into her heart.

With a laser-like force it burned away the golden net of enchantment that sensual voice had been weaving around her. India brought her head up sharply, repulsing his lingering caress with a violent jerk of her chin.

'Next few weeks of *what*?'

A new quirk to his mouth told her that he knew only too well that she had heard him perfectly the first time.

'You're in trouble, India. You need help.'

He sounded so damned reasonable that she almost believed he was on her side after all.

'Maybe I do, but not from you! I don't want your help; I'd rather die! I don't want *anything* from you.'

With rough, jerky movements she picked up the teatowel he had used, and began to wipe an imaginary puddle of water from the work-top.

'Not even a roof over your head—and your family's?'

That brought her up short, stilling her hand as she stared at him in frank bewilderment.

'I beg your pardon?'

To add to her confusion, it seemed that just for a second Aidan actually looked disconcerted. At the very least, he put on a fair act of feeling that way as he raked one strong hand through the sleek darkness of his hair.

'Well, what I've learned about your father means that I won't be able to go back to London for a while. I shall have to stay in Westbury, at least until he's well enough to talk to me, so I'll need somewhere to live.'

'There are plenty of hotels. After all, you're already booked into one.'

India had a horrible suspicion that she knew exactly what was coming.

'But it seems a terrible waste when the Grange has all these spare rooms.'

'None of which is available to you!'

To emphasise the point, she marched to the door and flung it open. But Aidan made no move to act on the obvious hint that he should leave.

'I want to stay here.' His tone was as ruthless and unyielding as his face.

'And I said I'd rather die than let you! Look—' she struggled for some degree of calm '—you're a very rich man; you can stay wherever you want.'

'But I wasn't always rich—and one of the first things I learned is that if you want to make a fortune you don't fritter away any hard-earned cash. Only a fool would spend money on accommodation when he has a house with seven bedrooms available.'

'When he has...?' India said shakily, praying that he hadn't meant what she'd thought.

Heaven ignored her pleas. Instead, Aidan gave a curt nod of his dark head, a grim smile curling the corners of his mouth.

'*This* house, to be precise.'

A couple of strides brought him to the door, but only to pull it from her unresisting grasp and close it firmly again, the gesture seeming to underline his words with ominous emphasis.

'I would have preferred it if you had found out in another way, but really I have no option now. To be perfectly blunt, you're attacking the wrong man. Your father is the one to blame in all this.'

'Well, isn't that just typical? I knew you hated him, but to blame him now, when he's ill and weak and can't answer for himself…!'

'No, India, it's the truth. He was the one who got himself—and you—into this mess.'

'What mess?' India croaked. She had the nastiest feeling that the ground was about to open up and swallow her.

'When I said your father owed me money, I wasn't just talking about the odd hundred—or even a couple of thousand. You must know that the situation is worse than that. It always was, even when we were together. His gambling…'

'Oh, I know he bet on the horses sometimes.'

A bitter understatement, that. It seemed that her father had been prepared to bet on anything that moved, and the account he had run up at the village bookmaker's had made her blood run cold.

'But he would never have come to you for help!'

'No, I realise that would have stuck in his throat, but he didn't have the choice.'

Aidan dismissed her protest with a contemptuous flick of his hand.

'Your papa has been spending time at a casino in Carleton—a lot of time—and he's been losing pretty heavily. But then, about six months ago, he had an unexpected run of good luck. Anyone with any sense would have taken their winnings and run, but not Bruce Marchant. *He* thought he was set to restore the family fortunes, and make a healthy profit to boot. So he bet all the money he'd won and a great deal that he hadn't.'

That sounded like Dad, India acknowledged with a dreary sense of inevitability. He was always looking for an easy way to make money, always envious of those who had. As a result he had always been a sucker for any get-rich-quick scheme that came his way, whether it looked sensible or not.

'Would you like to sit down?' Aidan had seen how the blood had left her cheeks. 'You might find it easier...'

He pulled out a chair from the table for her to use, but India refused to even look at it.

'Just tell me the worst!' she muttered through gritted teeth.

'All right. In the end your father lost everything he had and a small fortune on top. Then he signed IOUs as if they were Christmas cards, and pledged almost everything he possessed as security.'

'And just how do you know all this?'

'I own that casino,' Aidan returned grimly. 'All your father's IOUs are made out to me.'

For an amount that even the Lone Wolfe, with all his wealth, acknowledged as a fortune.

She had never known that Aidan actually owned a casino. When she'd first met him he had told her that he was looking for potential investment opportunities in the area, but he had never been inclined to go into details.

In the past she had wondered if his reticence had been because of her father's attitude, although she had never believed that Aidan would swallow Bruce Marchant's prejudice against money earned through trade as opposed to being inherited. But now she was forced to recall Aidan's earlier comment about her not caring *where* his money came from as long as there was plenty of it.

'And the security?' Did she have to ask?

Aidan's emotionless voice confirmed her worst fears.

'He put up this house against all his debts. When he lost,

I gave him six months to come up with the money before I took final possession. That was why I've been trying to get in touch with your father all week. The six months' grace was up two days ago. As of last Sunday, I own this house and everything in it.'

CHAPTER FIVE

'So IT's all true?'

India knew that she was clutching at straws. The look on the face of the man opposite her told her that.

Fred Curran, senior partner in the law firm where Jim worked, had been the family solicitor for years, and his expression told her that there was no room for hope. But she still had to ask.

'It's true, legal and all perfectly above board.'

The words fell, sounding a death-knell to her peace of mind, dark, sombre and totally irrefutable.

'Aidan Wolfe owns Westbury Grange?'

Somehow even saying the words out loud didn't make it seem any more possible or believable. But she had to accept that it was so. Everything was as Aidan had said. Her father had signed away their house—the only home that she and her mother and brother had ever known—in order to pay his gambling debts.

'Don't take my word for it,' Aidan had tossed at her the day before when she had refused to believe his outrageous declaration. 'Check it out. Talk to your lawyer if you like.'

And of course she had done just that; not that it had done her much good. When Aidan had talked of IOUs, she had imagined scrappy bits of paper hastily scribbled in the smoky, heated atmosphere of the casino—unable to hold water, let alone stand up to inspection in a court of law. But she had been very much mistaken.

Which, she acknowledged bitterly, she should really have known from the start. After all, this was Aidan Wolfe she was dealing with, the man whose ruthless prowess in the business world was legendary.

So the documents his lawyers had drawn up were as hard and unyielding as the man himself, legally binding, totally inescapable in any way. There was no room left for any doubt at all. Westbury Grange was the property of Aidan Wolfe. The Marchants no longer had a home there—or anywhere at all. And she shivered in cold fear at the way that her father's foolish action had put her family so completely in Aidan's power.

'All right, you've proved your case!' she flung at Aidan that evening when, as arranged, he called at the Grange to hear what she had to say.

He had reverted to the more formal clothes she was used to seeing him in, she realised, reluctantly opening the door wider to let him in. The strangely unsettling, more casual-looking Aidan had vanished, hidden under an impeccably tailored light grey suit worn with a crisp white shirt, the burgundy silk tie the only touch of colour in the whole outfit.

'All I ask is that you give us—say—seven days' grace.'

'A week?'

Aidan lifted a lazily questioning eyebrow as he strolled into the hallway, obviously totally at ease, and looking for all the world as if he owned the place—which of course he did, India reminded herself.

'What do you need so much time for? I would have thought that an hour at most...'

'A *hour*!'

Was the man a complete brute? She had known he could be cruel and ruthless, but this cold-blooded vindictiveness...

'I haven't even told my mother yet!'

She hadn't been able to bring herself to think of doing so, at least not until she knew there was no alternative. Her mother had already been through enough. To be told that her marital home had been gambled away and that she was expected to move out would devastate her.

'And it will take a while for us to pack,' she continued through lips that seemed to be made of wood, they were so stiff and tight. 'I mean, I know you own the house, but there are personal things...'

'Why should you want to pack?'

Aidan's confusion appeared almost genuine. Certainly, if she hadn't known him better, she might actually have been convinced.

'Well, of course you'll expect us to move out.'

'Whatever gave you that idea? For one thing, you've nowhere to go.'

She didn't need reminding of that fact, India thought, gritting her teeth against a furious outburst. She had spent all day racking her brains, trying to think of somewhere they could camp out—for a while, at least—until they found lodgings. And what would happen when her father was discharged from hospital?

'Don't be ridiculous, India. There's no need for you to go anywhere at all. There's plenty of room here. All I need is somewhere to sleep and work.'

India blinked in shocked disbelief. 'Are you offering...?'

'I'm inviting you to be my guest.'

Oh, how he'd enjoyed that! How he'd loved putting across that pointed reminder that *he* was the one in the position of being able to offer the invitation to stay at the Grange, the house in which her father had always made him feel so unwelcome in the past.

'I'd rather sleep in a Salvation Army hostel!' she flared in bitter resentment.

'Well, if that's your choice...' Aidan shrugged off her defiance. 'Of course, no one can stop you. But I do think you should consider your mother.'

India's mouth actually fell open at his audacity.

'Isn't that something of the pot calling the kettle black?'

'On the contrary,' Aidan returned with immovable calm, 'did you really think I was going to put you all out on the street without a second thought? What sort of monster do you think I am?'

'The sort who walks out on his bride in the middle of their wedding!' India flashed.

'Ah, but we've already established that it was no great love match. Now, do you think that we could continue this discussion in comfort?' His gesture indicated the door into the sitting room.

'If we must!'

Unwillingly India pushed open the door. Aidan followed her into the large, sunny room and immediately crossed to the window to look out at the glorious rose garden that lay just beyond it.

'I always agreed with your mother that this was the nicest room in the whole house,' he said, surprisingly softly. 'She would be heartbroken if she had to leave. Admit it, Princess. The last thing your mother needs is any further distress or strain. She already has quite enough on her plate as it is.'

'She certainly couldn't cope with knowing that you're hounding my father—'

'*No!*'

India flinched back in panic as the single explosive syllable brought Aidan swinging round, brown eyes blazing. Hastily she took several nervous steps backwards, away from him, but he came after her. Three swift strides brought him to within reach, and his hand shot out, fastening around her wrist, imprisoning her.

'I did not *hound* your father, Princess.'

He actually shook her—not hard enough to hurt, but with enough force to make her unnervingly aware of his strength and the rigid control he was imposing on it.

'If I had done that, I would have known exactly where he was and that he was ill. I gave him six months to come up with the money, and in that time I waited for him to come to me, damn it! It was only when he didn't that I came up here to find out what was going on.'

'And I'll bet you just loved that feeling of power, of having him at your mercy. You must have enjoyed getting your revenge—'

'Revenge for what?' Aidan cut in harshly. 'For the way he tried to stop me marrying you? Why should I want revenge for something I'd decided I never wanted in the first place?'

Even now, with the wounds scarred over by twelve months' distance, the knowledge of how little he'd really cared could catch her on the raw, searing agonisingly over barely healed lacerations in her heart. With a movement that echoed the turmoil of her thoughts she wrenched herself free, hastily putting one of the faded red brocade armchairs between her and Aidan.

'You'd be deceiving yourself if you thought it was like that, darling. Your father got himself into this mess all on his own.'

'It was your casino.'

'And I suppose I made your father go there?' Behind her, Aidan's voice was dark with cynical mockery. 'I put a gun to his head and forced him to bet all he owned?'

'No.' Reluctantly India forced herself to face him again. But meeting those bitter chocolate eyes was more than she could manage. 'But you could have refused to accept any more bets.'

'I could.' Aidan's voice was a harsh whiplash that seemed to scour the skin from her back. 'But this time I chose not to. I thought perhaps it was time someone taught him a lesson.'

'You couldn't wait to get him into your clutches, you mean! And of course, once you'd done that, you had the perfect opportunity to get your hands on the Grange—without having to go to the trouble of marrying into the family.'

Her words stirred unwanted memories of the time after she had first brought Aidan home. She could hear her father's voice as clearly as if he were in the room, speaking to her now.

'If you ask me, he's after what you can bring him. If anything motivates him it's greed, not love.'

She had laughed in his face, foolishly confident in her belief that Aidan really cared. 'Don't be ridiculous, Dad! Aidan already has more money than he knows what to do with. What do I have that he could possibly want?'

She had forgotten Aidan's reaction the first time he had ever seen the Grange. Forgotten the stunned look that had come into his eyes, the muttered exclamation that had escaped him.

'What is this, Aidan?' she asked sharply now. 'Did you take a fancy to the place when you were dating me? And, knowing Dad's weakness for gambling…'

She'd hit on something there, she realised with a stab of bitterness as she saw something change in those dark eyes. Just for a second Aidan refused to meet her searching gaze, his brown eyes sliding away from her green ones and staring out of the window into the gathering twilight in an oddly unfocused way.

'I'll admit that I fell in love with this place as soon as I saw it.'

With the house, India acknowledged drearily. Not with herself.

'But if you're thinking that's why I wanted to marry you, then think again. After all, I could buy a house like the Grange many times over.'

'A house like the Grange. But not *the Grange* itself.'

Her taunt dried to a squeak as, with a muttered curse, Aidan kicked the chair out of the way and curled a powerful hand around her wrist again.

'If you think like that…'

As he spoke he was dragging her with him, pulling her from the room, through the hallway and out into the garden. In spite of her attempt to dig in her heels and resist him,

India had no choice but to follow, incapable of fighting the whipcord strength of his arms.

'It's time you looked at things as they really are!'

With a violent jerk of his arm, Aidan swung her round so that she was facing the house.

'Look at it!' he commanded harshly. 'Really look, damn you!'

India didn't need to look. She was only too well aware of the way that the Grange had been neglected, aware of the crumbling brickwork and rotten windowframes. If vital repair work wasn't done soon then the beautiful old house that she loved so much would fall into rack and ruin.

'Do you actually think that this place is a worthwhile investment? The garden's a jungle, the plumbing archaic, and every window in the place needs replacing. And, unless you had some appalling set of cowboys in to do the job last year, the tiles haven't been touched since I was here then.'

'We couldn't afford it,' India muttered.

'I'll bet.' His tone was pure cynicism, blended with something else—something India couldn't interpret. 'This house will fall down round your ears if something isn't organised quickly. Does the roof still leak so badly?'

India could only nod silently, not wanting to recall the happy, rain-lashed afternoon they had spent investigating the junk piled in the Grange's huge attics which had led to Aidan becoming aware of that particular problem.

But the memory was already there, bright and clear in her mind as if it had happened only the day before. It had been during that week when her parents had been away, and on the one day they had actually emerged from her room, from her bed. Aidan had insisted on exploring the Grange from top to bottom.

'If you'd seen where I grew up, then you'd realise just how amazing this place is,' he had enthused.

He had been staggered by the size of the attics, and by

the amount of stuff stored up there in boxes and trunks or elderly chests of drawers.

'Your school reports from year dot, Princess!' he had exclaimed, pulling papers out of a folder. '"India is an asset to the junior choir." You never told me you could sing!'

'Ah!' India slanted a brilliant, teasing smile at him. 'I didn't want you to discover all my talents at once!'

Her laughter caught in her throat as she saw the way Aidan's eyes darkened, heard the sudden smokiness of his voice as he murmured, 'The ones you've already shown me are more than enough to keep me happy for now.'

'Do I get an A grade?' India's question was slightly breathless as the result of the way her heart was beating, thudding with excitement high up in her chest. It was only a couple of hours since they had got out of bed, but already she was hungry for him again. 'Or perhaps a gold star? No?' She couldn't believe it when he shook his head.

'Could try harder,' Aidan pronounced with unnerving seriousness. But then, just as she was beginning to feel distinctly worried, his mood changed abruptly, the corners of his mouth curling up into a wide, brilliant grin. 'What you need is some intensive individual coaching—one to one.'

'Oh, you—!'

Realising how easily she had been duped, she whirled away, snatching up whatever was closest to hand and flinging it at him. Laughter bubbled up inside her as folds of pale pink material tangled around his head, and he had to pull himself free, emerging from its confines to direct a mock glare at her. The ferocity of his look was contradicted by the gleam in his eyes, the curve to his lips.

'You'll pay for that, madam!'

The sensual undertone to the threat made India's heart lurch in excited response at the thought of just what type of retribution he would subject her to. The pink dress had ruffled his hair, destroying its usually severely smooth style, and her hands itched to tangle with the dark strands, feel their silkiness slide under her fingertips as it had done so many times in the night.

'I'll— What the hell *is* this?'

'Let me see.'

Coming closer, India examined the pink and lace creation he held out to her.

'A party dress. The one I wore for my seventh birthday, I think.'

'Your seventh…'

India watched as Aidan pulled open two more drawers of the chest in front of him, shaking his head in bemusement at what he saw there.

'Your parents must have collected everything you've ever worn.'

'Mmm…'

It was almost impossible to concentrate on what he was saying. A shaft of sunlight had slanted through the skylight in the roof, playing over Aidan's tall frame in the blue shirt and navy trousers. It ran like a stream of gold over the strong lines of his body, highlighting the broad shoulders, powerful chest and narrow waist—and India felt her mouth dry with excitement at the memory of how it had felt to have all that magnificent masculine force intimately entangled with her own limbs during the night.

'Even your baby shoes.'

The tiny items looked positively microscopic dangling from one large hand, but all India could think of was the intense pleasure those tanned fingers could create with the lightest touch on her breasts, her thighs.

Moving forward, she plucked the shoes from Aidan's grasp, dumping them back in the drawer before sliding her body up against his and putting her arms around his waist, hands linked in the small of his back.

'Of course,' she murmured indifferently. 'Didn't your parents save all your baby things?'

It was a mistake; she knew that as soon as she had spoken. Something had destroyed the light-hearted mood,

Aidan's long body stiffening suddenly, putting an emotional distance between them that was in stark contrast to their physical closeness.

'My parents didn't go in for that sort of thing,' he declared curtly. 'They weren't like your family at all. They—had other preoccupations.'

What *were* they like? Why do you never talk about them? The questions almost escaped India, but hastily she caught them back, afraid to ask them. She had never heard that tone of voice from him before, and it frightened her. Suddenly Aidan had become a dark, distant stranger, and she didn't know how to handle him in this mood.

Or did she? Feminine instinct gave her inspiration, and she snuggled closer, resting her head against his chest. She felt his tension, the sudden change in his breathing, and smiled to herself at the thought that she was having just the effect she wanted.

Loosening her hands, she ran them over his chest, toying with the buttons on his shirt, letting her fingers slip in at its open neck to trace delicate patterns on the satin warmth of his skin.

'India…' Aidan growled, but whether in warning or encouragement she couldn't decide.

It was safer to interpret it as the latter, and so she pressed even closer, sliding her pelvis against his in deliberate provocation.

'I think we've been up here long enough,' she murmured with soft petulance. 'Why don't we go back downstairs…?'

Another sensual little wriggle brought her into contact with the hard evidence of the physical effect she was having on him, and her smile grew.

'We could do something much more interesting.'

'India—you shouldn't—' For the space of a couple of heartbeats longer he resisted, but then suddenly, and with a muttered, 'God, Princess, but when I'm with you I can't think straight!' he bent his dark head and crushed her lips under his.

'I don't want you to *think*,' India purred a couple of seconds later as he swung her up into his arms and carried her towards the stairs down to her bedroom. 'I much prefer action.'

It was far too late now to wish that she had let him continue, India admitted to herself, looking at Aidan and seeing that same distant, withdrawn expression on his face now.

You shouldn't... Shouldn't what? Shouldn't trust him? Shouldn't let herself fall in love? Was it possible that at that point his conscience had actually pricked him and he had been about to tell her the truth about how little he felt for her?

She would never know. Certainly the Aidan she was dealing with now showed no sign of any such uncomfortable attacks of morality—if that had been what it was. Instead he had no compunction at all about what he was doing.

'The wiring's out of the ark.' Aidan's attention was still on the house and its faults.

'I'll get someone onto that straight away.'

And he would do just that, India knew. When Aidan Wolfe said something was going to be done, then it was done without the slightest delay or he wanted to know the reason why.

'And you actually thought that I would go to the trouble of plotting and scheming in order to get my hands on *that*?' An arrogant wave of his hand dismissed the Grange as a worthless pile of junk.

'That's my home you're talking about!'

India's voice was high and tight with a bitter mixture of indignation and pain. With just the same sort of autocratic carelessness he had dismissed her from his life when he had tired of her—and with the echoes of other, happier times still in her mind it was almost more than she could bear.

'Whose home, India?' It was soft, almost gentle, but threaded through with a darkly sardonic note.

That was too much.

'You don't have to rub it in, you bastard!'

Beside herself with fury, she launched her free hand at his face, only to miss his lean cheek by a mile. Aidan had sidestepped neatly, twisting the arm he held until she was imprisoned hard up against him.

'India…'

India ignored his quiet use of her name, aiming a wild kick at his leg. She took a grim satisfaction in hearing his grunt of pain as her foot made contact with his ankle.

'India, I'm sorry.' The voice that finally penetrated the red haze in her mind was disturbingly soft, as were the hands that now enclosed her own, easing her imprisonment. 'That was cruel.'

I'm sorry! India's mind reeled in disbelief. Had the Lone Wolfe actually said those words? Had he really apologised for his behaviour?

'I know how much this place means to you, and I promise I'll take care of it.'

I promise. Two words guaranteed to drive all the fight from her. During their brief courtship, that phrase had had the sort of value she would have staked her life on. If Aidan had promised anything, he had always delivered—except on one vital occasion.

And then, of course, he hadn't actually given his word. He hadn't stayed around to promise to love and honour her, to remain faithful until death.

'I only want to restore it, not launch into some appalling modernisation. You do believe that, don't you?'

India found the answer to that question surprisingly easy.

'Yes.' She nodded, still keeping her face averted. 'I believe you. I—trust you with the Grange.'

With her home—but never, ever with her heart. But then she heard a sound that was like a heartfelt sigh, so soft that he couldn't even be sure it hadn't been just her imagination.

'Thank you for that, at least,' Aidan said roughly. 'I thought that in your eyes I was totally irredeemable.'

Lifting her head in surprise, India saw something change behind his eyes, some sudden flash of a raw emotion that seemed to match her own. It was only fleeting, gone in a second. But it gave her the push to ask the question that wouldn't leave her mind.

'*Did* you ever want to marry me?' she asked sharply, searching his face for the vital answer. 'Or was it all just deceit from the start?'

For a long, uncomfortable moment she thought he wasn't going to deign to give her an answer. But then he gave a small, grim smile that made her heart clench.

'I always believed that marriage wasn't for me, but you came close to making me change my mind. From the moment I met you, my sweet India, the only thing I knew for sure was that I couldn't keep my hands off you, and it seemed you felt the same. And that magic is still there.'

The fragile moment of understanding was shattered, destroyed by his tone and the cold-hearted frankness of his declaration.

'Magic!' India echoed cynically, fighting to suppress the way her mind replayed erotic images of the scene in the kitchen the day before. 'That's something of an exaggeration.'

Aidan's smile was positively beatific, in unnerving contrast to the devilishly wicked gleam in his eyes.

'I don't have to exaggerate,' he drawled lazily. 'My memory is perfectly clear, and, believe me, it needs no embellishment. Which will make our living together so much more interesting.'

'Well, memories are all you're going to have.' Belatedly she realised that he still held her hands, and she snatched them away abruptly. 'And we won't be *living together*! We haven't resolved anything…'

'There's nothing to resolve,' Aidan stated calmly 'You've already admitted that you can't afford to move anywhere else, and we both know that your mother couldn' cope with any further strain.'

He had moved across to one of the ground-floor window; as he spoke, and was now examining it closely, frowning slightly as he saw how the paint had flaked away in places exposing the raw wood.

'You'd tell her?'

'Only if you force me to.'

It came almost lightly, but with a dark undertone o threat that made India mentally flinch away from the im plications of a possible challenge to his authority on this.

'And if you can't think of her, what about your father' I asked at the hospital this morning, and they said he'; showing signs of coming out of the coma. The next few days could be critical.'

'You asked…! But they wouldn't give that sort of in formation out to just anyone!'

But, of course, Aidan Wolfe wasn't 'just anyone'.

'They would when I explained that I was your fiancé. Turning slowly, he surveyed India's indignant face with lazy indulgence. 'And that's who I intend to be for the nex few weeks.'

'No way!'

Aidan ignored her choking cry of impotent fury.

'I'm sorry, Princess, but that point isn't up for negotia tion. In return for my generosity in letting you stay here, get to move into the Grange and live as part of the family.

'No…' That was too much to ask.

'Oh, yes, my lovely. It's the only way it'll work. You mother has to believe that we're reconciled—that all's righ between us once again—otherwise she'll start to smell very large rat. If you want a roof over your head in th coming weeks, then you have to do something to earn i You have to act as if all is forgiven and forgotten.'

'I can't!'

'And convince everyone that we're once again a couple,' Aidan continued as if she hadn't spoken. 'But then, you won't find it too difficult to take on the part of the loving fiancée. You passed the audition with flying colours.'

She couldn't do it! And yet if she didn't then Aidan would put her and her mother and brother out onto the street.

He was perfectly capable of carrying out his threat, she knew. There was no point in throwing herself on his mercy. You didn't do that with the Lone Wolfe. He was far more likely to tear you to little pieces, chew you up and spit you out again with the blunt declaration that frankly you weren't at all to his taste.

And she was in no doubt as to what he had meant by her 'audition'. Once again, the scene in the kitchen played inside her head, devastating in its sensual impact.

'I'll not share your bed!' she cried, and saw one dark eyebrow lift in cynical response to her outburst.

'Might I suggest that you wait until you're asked?' he drawled tauntingly. 'Whatever else you may think of me, darling, I have never had to stoop to buying my women, or forcing them. I have rather more pride than that.'

The relief was like a shock wave to her brain—a lifting of pressure so swift and intense that for a moment she could only smile her delight straight into his watchful eyes, her own green ones glowing brilliantly.

But that feeling evaporated swiftly as she saw his harsh-featured face darken, his eyes becoming impenetrable.

'Not that I don't think it's on the cards,' he added, with a smile that turned her blood to ice. 'In my opinion it's *when,* not *if.* It's as inevitable as the sun rising tomorrow morning, and all I have to do is wait. But we'll let that develop in its own sweet time, as I'm sure it will.'

'Then you'll wait till hell freezes over!' India flashed at him, her eyes blazing and her chin coming up in furious rejection of his darkly gloating confidence. 'I'll never...'

'You know what they say about never saying never,'

Aidan put in warningly. 'Be careful, Princess, you might live to regret it.'

A second later he switched on a blinding smile that was positively lethal to what remained of her shattered self-control.

'And now that that's settled, I'll go and fetch my bags from the car. Then you can show me which is my room.'

'You've got your bags with you!'

'Well, naturally.'

Aidan had started towards the drive, heading for where he had parked his car. But now he stopped and turned back, that smile growing wider, dazzlingly so.

'I checked out of the hotel this morning.'

'You were so sure of yourself?' Her whole body seemed to turn to ice at the thought.

'Oh, no, my sweet India.'

Aidan's voice was suddenly worryingly low and gentle.

'I wasn't sure of myself, darling, but of you. You see, sweetheart, unlike your father, I only ever bet very, very carefully. I would never put my money on anything but an obvious winner—and in this case I knew I had a certainty.'

CHAPTER SIX

'GARY! Where are you?'

Damn the boy! India fumed. Just where had he disappeared to this time? She had drawn a blank when she had looked for him in his bedroom, and again in the lounge. She was just about to try the garden when the sound of laughter from the back of the house drew her attention. Immediately she turned and headed for the kitchen door.

'So this is where you've been hiding! I've been looking for you everywhere! Really, Gary...'

Her voice died in her throat, her feet coming to an abrupt halt as she rounded the corner of the house. Taking in the scene before her in one swift, disturbed glance, she realised what she should have known from the start—Gary was not alone.

Aidan was with her brother, obviously having taken a rare break from supervising the renovation work that had already started on the house. They had set up makeshift goals on the long lawn at the back of the house, and had obviously been playing football for some time. Their foreheads and the backs of their T-shirts were damp with sweat as a result of the exertion in the warmth of the afternoon, and both Aidan's jeans and her brother's shorts were stained with grass and dirt.

Just as she appeared, Gary launched into an over-enthusiastic tackle that sent Aidan flying, his feet going from under him. Gary, too, was unable to keep his balance, and they fell in a laughing heap directly in India's path. Propelled with force, the ball crashed into the shrubbery behind one set of goalposts.

'Goal!' Breathless with exertion and laughter, Gary lifted one fist in a gesture of triumph. 'Three-nil!'

'No way!' Aidan protested indignantly. 'You're not getting away with that! It was a blatant foul—don't you agree, ref?'

It took a couple of seconds for India to realise that the question was directed at her. Aidan's dark eyes, warm with amusement, were fixed on her face as he disentangled himself from Gary's sprawling limbs and got to his feet, yanking her brother up behind him.

'I—'

Her heart clenched as she registered how in that moment Aidan seemed almost as young as her brother, enjoyment lighting his face, obliterating the cold, severe lines in which it was usually set. His eyes glowed and his mouth was stretched into a delighted smile.

That wide grin combined with the gleam of the sunlight on his dark hair and the flush of colour in his cheeks to strike like an arrow straight at her heart.

'I don't know. I wasn't watching.'

'It was a goal!' Gary declared again, and Aidan laughed at his indignant face, ruffling the boy's dark hair with a casual hand.

'In your dreams, sunshine! I have never seen—or, rather, felt—a more deliberate foul in my life, as I'm sure your sister—'

'Don't bring me into this!' India put in hastily. 'I told you, I wasn't looking.'

Not true, her conscience reproached her. She hadn't been able to take her eyes off Aidan. It had been impossible not to recall with sharp clarity the last time she had seen him look so vividly, so youthfully alive—not the cold, controlled man who had come back into her life.

On that occasion *she* had been the one lying with him—though she had been underneath, not on top like Gary. And they most definitely had not been playing football. It had been games of a very different kind that had been on both their minds.

It had been just a few days before the wedding, a time when, with thoughts of fastening the close-fitting bodice of her dress very much in her mind, she had been watching everything she ate. One brilliantly hot afternoon, Aidan had deliberately tempted her with her favourite ice cream, indulging in a large, delicious-looking cone that had made her mouth water just to see it.

In the end, temptation had overcome her resistance and, choosing a moment when Aidan was distracted, she had snatched the cone from his hand, grinning wickedly at his roar of protest.

'You little witch! Give that back!'

'Come and get it!'

With laughter bubbling up inside her, she took to her heels, Aidan in hot pursuit. The chase took them away from the crowded lakeside, where they were spending the afternoon after having lunch in a restaurant there, and up into the shade of a wooded hillside.

It was there that, catching her foot in a twisted root, India slipped and would have fallen hard onto the sun-parched grass. But Aidan was closer behind her than she realised. He saw her danger and acted quickly, his long body cushioning her fall, a faint grunt of reaction escaping him as she landed on his chest and legs, driving all the breath from him for a second.

India, too, felt as if she couldn't breathe. But her reaction was much more the result of the feel of the heat and hardness of the powerful frame beneath her, the strength of the arms that had closed round her waist, than anything to do with her emotions.

Her heart, already racing after her run, lurched into a frantic pulse that made her blood pound through her veins. Deliberately she moved on Aidan, writhing sensually, a secret smile curving her lips as she felt his immediate and very physical response.

'You little witch!' he growled in her ear, with a very different intonation this time, his breath hot against her skin. 'I can't get enough of you.'

Her smile widening, intoxicated by the power she had over him, India wriggled again. Aidan muttered a thick-voiced curse, his arms tightening. The next moment, in one swift movement, he reversed their positions so that she was underneath him, the full weight of his body pressing her into the ground, his mouth just inches away from hers and his eyes, burning with dark fire, all she could see...

'Indy?' Gary's voice jolted her out of her memories and back into the present.

India was thoroughly disconcerted to find that her pulse rate had quickened in an echo of the way she had felt in her thoughts. Her breathing was almost as uneven as her brother's after his exertions.

She was supremely conscious of Aidan close by, so tall and dark and devastatingly male in the clinging T-shirt and jeans. The watchful gaze of those brown eyes felt almost like a physical burn on her skin. And when he moved suddenly she actually flinched in instinctive response, even though he had only lifted a hand to rake the sweat-dampened hair back from his forehead.

'What was it you wanted?'

'I...'

For an uncomfortable couple of seconds her mind went disturbingly blank. For the life of her she couldn't recall just what had brought her out here. All she was aware of was a tiny bead of moisture on Aidan's cheek and a terrible, almost overwhelming need to reach out and wipe it away with a gentle fingertip.

But then he moved again, brushing the back of his hand over his face, and her thought processes jerked into life once more.

'You promised to help with supper tonight, Gary. There's a load of potatoes that need peeling.'

'Oh, but, Sis...!'

'Oh, but, nothing!' The knowledge that Aidan was still watching her and the fear that her feelings might show on her face made her voice tarter than she had intended.

'Meals don't cook themselves. So let's have you in the kitchen as soon as you've cleaned yourself up.'

It was a relief to escape, to make her way back to the kitchen, exerting all the self-control she possessed in order to bring her breathing back to normal. Anyone would think that she had been the one playing football.

Would she ever get used to Aidan's presence in her home? *His* home, she corrected herself furiously. It had been five days now since he had moved in, and she was nowhere near accepting it.

Her mood was so thoroughly rattled that she banged lids onto pans, slamming them down onto the stove with a crash. Giving up on Gary, she was about to start on the potatoes herself when the door finally opened behind her.

'At last! Where did you get to?'

'You did say "as soon as you get cleaned up",' pointed out a voice that was very definitely not Gary's, making her spin round in shock.

'Aidan! But I was expecting…'

'Gary. I know,' Aidan supplied when she couldn't finish the sentence. 'But there was something he wanted to watch on television so I said I'd act as chef's assistant instead.'

'But you…'

If she had been unsettled before, now things were so much worse. Aidan had obviously come to the kitchen fresh from the shower. His dark hair was still damp and swept back from his face, emphasising the impact of his strongly carved face, and he looked fresh, invigorated and vibrantly alive.

The crisp white shirt he wore with a clean pair of jeans made India painfully conscious of the fact that her simple green dress was already rather the worse for wear as a result of her earlier clumsiness with the pans. With her black hair pulled back into a loose ponytail and a touch of mascara her only make-up, she felt scruffy, ill-groomed and distinctly unglamorous.

'You're really feeling hard done by, are you?' To her astonishment Aidan actually sounded amused. 'Well, it's your own fault, lady. If you wanted help, you only had to say. Move over.'

The potato peeler was taken from her grasp, and strong hands moved her gently but firmly to one side so that he could take her place at the sink.

'No—I mean, you can't...'

'I'm perfectly capable of peeling a few potatoes, India,' Aidan responded calmly, misunderstanding the reasons for her spluttered protest—deliberately, she was sure.

'I'm sure you are, but...'

'But?' Aidan prompted when her throat seemed to close over the words that she wanted to form so that she was unable to get them past the tight knot of resistance. His closeness meant that when he moved she caught a trace of some light, tangy aftershave, mixed with the clean, personal scent of his body to create a devastating impact that rocked her already shaky mental balance.

'You shouldn't have to help out,' she managed by sheer force of will. 'After all, you do own the Grange now.'

'And how it sticks in your throat to admit that.'

Aidan's voice was suddenly harsh, and it was only now, when it had vanished completely, that she realised there had been a very different expression on his face only moments before, one that had been replaced by icy contempt.

'Tell me...'

Unexpectedly Aidan's tone had reverted to its earlier casualness. But his hands, employing the potato peeler with a swift, ruthless efficiency, betrayed the truth of his inner feelings.

'Have I ever made you or any member of your family feel that you weren't welcome here? Or that I expected anything at all in return for your staying in the house?'

'No.'

She couldn't say anything else. Since he had moved into the Grange Aidan had been discretion personified—at least as far as his ownership of the Grange was concerned. She knew that her mother suspected nothing of the truth, being blithely unaware of the undercurrents that darkened the glow of this unexpected upturn in their family fortunes.

But India was only too well aware of those dark eddies, could feel them swirling around her ankles, threatening to drag her down.

She had sensed them pulling at her like the suck of quicksand all the time she had been standing at Aidan's side earlier that week, when her mother had returned from the hospital and found them together. India had been forced to listen to Aidan's explanation of his presence in the house, knowing that her silence supported his lies.

'Business brought me into the area,' he had said, and, if she hadn't known precisely what that 'business' was, India felt that she too would have thought his appearance in Westbury was purely by chance. 'And I heard of your husband's illness. Naturally, I was shocked and concerned, so I called at the house to see if there was anything I could do to help. As soon as I saw India again, I realised what a terrible mistake I had made last year...'

Her mother had swallowed it all, India recalled bitterly. Swallowed that and all the rest of the embroidery that had followed, believing Aidan when he said how much he regretted what had happened.

'It was a silly quarrel we had; a lovers' spat. You know the sort of thing—how pre-wedding nerves build problems up out of all proportion until it only takes one more straw to push things right over the edge. But India's forgiven me—*haven't you*, darling?'

He didn't quite dig her hard in the ribs on the last question, but he might as well have done. And with her mother's eyes on her face, shining with the first hint of anything close to hope that India had seen in them for weeks, she knew she had no option but to nod enthusiastic agreement.

She felt like all sorts of a traitor when Marion Marchant moved to take both her hands.

'And is it all on again, then?' she asked, the quaver in her voice revealing how much this meant to her. 'Does this mean that you're engaged, and that…?'

'Ah, well, we don't want to rush things,' Aidan inserted smoothly, sensing as if by telepathy that India couldn't go quite as far as to agree to *that.*

'It's all a bit sudden, and totally unexpected. We want to take things slowly and carefully before we commit ourselves to anything. After all, I think that was probably what went wrong last time. We did rather rush into things without giving ourselves time to get to know each other. So, if you don't mind, we'd prefer to keep things to ourselves for a while. At least until we're sure of exactly how we feel about each other.'

And of course her mother had swallowed that too, hook, line and sinker. She had believed it all the more when Aidan, in the role once more of prospective son-in-law, had 'offered' to take on the responsibility for her father's job and all the repairs to the Grange that had become so urgently necessary.

It had been all that India could do not to be violently sick, or at least take some action to expose Aidan's cruel deception, her stomach heaving when she saw the falsely modest way he accepted Marion's heartfelt gratitude. But to reveal the truth would have been to cause her mother's new-found happiness to collapse in ashes at her feet.

'No, you haven't made us feel unwelcome,' India admitted now. 'But what you say and do has no significance when I know the truth about how things really are. We both know that all this is just a fantasy based on a total illusion. And one day, when it suits whatever plan you have up your sleeve, you're going to drop that deceitful mask of smiles and destroy my mother's happiness completely.'

The look Aidan turned on her was distinctly worrying, but she struggled to ignore it, forcing herself to go on.

'I mean, be honest. How long have we got before—'

'How long?' Aidan broke in, seeming to be considering his answer to the question, though India was sure he already knew perfectly well what it would be. 'Well, that's really up to you.'

'To me?'

He nodded coolly as he tossed a finished potato into the bowl beside the other vegetables she had already prepared.

'As long as you play your part properly, then there will be no need to disillusion your mother about the situation. But if she ever begins to suspect that things are not as she fondly believes…'

He let the sentence trail off, not completing the implied threat, but India knew there was no need for him to do any such thing.

'And by "playing my part properly", I suppose you mean that I should be—what? More demonstrative? More—amorous?'

She didn't like the gleam that lit up his eyes, the way his mouth quirked at the corner in response to that. A mocking lift of one dark eyebrow indicated that he was very well aware of the way that she was desperately trying to avoid the word 'loving' to describe the way she should behave.

It was only when she saw his reaction that she realised that her actual choice of words had sexual connotations that she definitely didn't want him to consider.

'A little more *warmth* wouldn't go amiss,' he drawled sardonically. 'I mean, no one's going to believe that we've had a genuine reconciliation if you continue to jump like a startled cat each time I come into the room, or run off to hide in the kitchen every evening—'

'I do not *hide*!' India protested.

Behind her, the ring of the timer on the oven gave her an excuse to move away and check on the contents of the casserole inside. By the time she turned back, she hoped that the heat from the cooker would explain her flushed cheeks and overbright eyes.

'Don't you think it would look more convincing if we did things together?' Aidan asked, finishing the last potato and adding it to the others.

'Together?' The prospect was not one she could face with any degree of equanimity. 'I can't get away from you as it is. If I go into the lounge you're there, in some chair with the paper.'

And his presence there, or at the table for family meals, was a constant bitter reminder of the dreams she had had this time last year. So many times she had pictured Aidan in her home in just this way—but as her husband, not as the intruder, the vindictive cuckoo that had well and truly taken over the nest. The thought of the destruction of those dreams was a constant raw pain in her heart.

'Or you're in the library, poring over the plans and estimates for all these alterations you've set in motion. And you expect me to discuss them with you.'

'I thought you'd be interested.' Aidan's tone was strangely flat. 'I didn't want to trample on your feelings, so I decided to include you in any consultation on the renovations.'

Renovations she would probably never see complete, India thought bitterly, the realisation rubbing salt into already bitterly painful wounds.

'It is your house,' she said stiffly.

'But you have such great taste. You know exactly what touches are needed to turn a house into a home—something I know very little about.'

Something in that last comment caught India on the raw. It reminded her of the way he had talked about his parents on that day in the attic.

She wanted to take him up on it, and yet didn't know how, afraid of stirring his anger by blundering into areas he preferred to keep strictly private. Instead, seeing that the bowl of unpeeled potatoes was empty, she took refuge in clumsy politeness.

'Well, thanks for your help tonight. I'm really grateful—'

She broke off nervously as Aidan threw the peeler onto the draining board with an ominous clatter.

'I don't want your gratitude for anything!' he flung at her, yellow flames of anger flaring in the depths of his eyes. But a second later he had collected himself again, adding with a lightness that took her breath away, 'And, believe me, peeling a few potatoes is hardly going to stretch my culinary skills to the limit.'

In spite of herself, India was intrigued.

'Do you have any? Culinary skills, I mean?'

'You'd better believe it. In fact, why don't you forget about cooking tomorrow night's meal and leave it all up to me? There's no need to look so sceptical, Princess,' he added tartly, seeing the response in her face, but misinterpreting the reasons for it. 'I may just surprise you.'

'You already have,' India admitted honestly.

The small exchange reminded her just how little she had actually known about Aidan before. If the truth was told, she had known little more than anyone who read the national tabloids. And yet she had been confident enough to believe that her future happiness lay with him.

Which just proved that love was blind, she told herself bitterly. Or, more accurately, in her case it had been lust that was blind, or blazing, unthinking desire. It had certainly blinded her to the truth, until her wedding day had opened her eyes once and for all.

Now, however, she saw him sharp and clear as never before—and what she found made shivers of fear run down her spine. Aidan Wolfe was every bit as physically devastating as before, but that imposing exterior hid a heart as black and cold as polished jet. He was the Lone Wolfe through and through, totally ruthless and ready to prey on anyone who showed themselves to be weaker than him.

But he was also the man who had enjoyed a carefree game of football with her kid brother, the man who had set to a simple kitchen task with no thought of preserving any macho image.

'You can cook?'

'Not only that, but I actually enjoy it.'

He managed the easy response much more successfully than she had done, but her attention wasn't fully on his words. She hadn't realised that he had been quite so close all this time. Or perhaps he had suddenly moved nearer in the past few moments, so that she could almost feel the warmth of his skin, hear the soft sound of his breathing.

His tall, lean body blocked out the light from the window, taking the warmth with it too, so that she suddenly felt cold as he towered over her worryingly. His very height and breadth seemed threatening, drying her mouth and making her shift uneasily, moving her weight from one foot to the other.

'And I have it on good authority that my lasagne is second to none.'

'Rich, handsome and talented too! The man has everything!'

India was barely aware of the words she spoke. It seemed that the real communication was going on on a much more basic, instinctive level. It was there in the darkness of his eyes, the intensity of his gaze, that seemed to scorch her skin where it rested.

Unwillingly, she felt her own body react to the closeness of his. Her heart lurched into an uneven, jerky pattern that made her breathing become raw and over-fast, her breasts rising and falling in betraying response.

'You really are quite a catch. You'll make some lucky woman a wonderful husband.'

The sudden icy glare he turned on her alerted her to the mistake she had made. Her breath hissed inwards sharply as she tensed, waiting for the inevitable reaction.

CHAPTER SEVEN

INDIA didn't have long to wait.

'*That* isn't on the cards.'

Cold and sharp as a blade of ice, the retort slashed into India's words, jolting her out of the sensual frame of mind she had fallen into. It was as if steel shutters had slammed shut behind his eyes, cutting his thoughts off from her.

In the same moment it seemed as if that burning awareness that had smouldered between them was now smothered as effectively as if someone had flung freezing water over them to douse it.

'Once bitten, twice shy?' she muttered.

Not that he had been 'bitten' in any way. Bitten implied a loss of control, a succumbing to irresistible forces outside yourself. Aidan had been fully in charge of his every action all the time, planning his moves with the care and anticipation of a master chess-player.

'If I ever felt tempted, then the fact that I can still feel the scars is enough to warn me off.'

'Scars!' India scoffed. 'The tiny scratches your ego received could hardly be described as wounds.' Unlike the deadly hurts he had inflicted on her.

'Well, you should know,' was the sardonic response. 'Now, what else needs doing?'

'What?' India found it hard to adjust to his swift change of topic and mood. 'Oh, there's just the table to set, but I can do that.'

Ignoring that comment, Aidan straightened up from where he had been leaning against the sink unit, and walked across the kitchen to the large Welsh dresser on the opposite side of the room. Pulling out the cutlery drawer, he

91

began to count out knives and forks, placing them on the tray laid ready for that purpose.

'So, has there been anyone…?'

'Since you?' Aidan gave an expressive shudder. 'No way. Been there, tried that, didn't bother to stay around to buy the T-shirt.'

'I would have thought that you'd see it as the perfect opportunity to go back to your old ways,' India returned waspishly, stung by his dark flippancy.

It was, after all, what she'd expected. She had nerved herself for the pain of seeing his picture in the papers once more, the inevitable model or film starlet on his arm. She had been frankly stunned when it hadn't happened.

'Lots of women?' He kept his attention fixed on what he was doing. 'Why not? A reputation as a stud is far easier to maintain than the myth of being a happily married man.'

'Easier on who? On you, perhaps—but what about the women you use?'

Too late she realised that this line of questioning was potentially dynamite. Since she had claimed a relationship with Jim to hide behind, it must have been painfully clear to Aidan that her supposed boyfriend hadn't played a large part in her life over the past days. So far he hadn't commented on it, but if she wasn't careful she was going to have to do some quick thinking in order to explain his absence.

'They give as good as they get. And you're a fine one to talk about *using*.'

'I didn't—'

'You didn't what?' Aidan suddenly lifted his head, looking into her face with a new and disturbing intensity. 'You didn't know that I was wealthy? Didn't see me as just what you were looking for? Didn't—?'

'All right, yes!' Driven beyond endurance, India broke in on him sharply. 'Yes! Yes! Yes!'

She didn't even know quite what it was she was admitting to, but didn't care. She only wanted to stop that cynical voice, put an end to his taunts.

Because now, when she was totally unprepared for it and didn't know how to handle it, she realised that her memory of the time she had stolen Aidan's ice cream and the resultant chase through the woods hadn't been complete. There was something she was forgetting, something the unwanted eroticism of her thoughts had driven from her mind. 'You little witch!' he had growled. 'I can't get enough of you. I can't wait until we're married and I can have you all to myself.'

She wasn't fooling herself now, seeing only what she wanted to see. At that moment, at least, Aidan had been happy to be with her. He had seemed to be anticipating their marriage with almost as much pleasure as she had felt. So what had happened to turn him into the cold-blooded monster of her wedding day?

'Yes, that was what I said I wanted at the beginning...' she said quietly.

Her nerve failed her as Aidan suddenly abandoned what he was doing and strode towards her. For an unnerving couple of seconds she thought he was actually going to take her in his arms. But at the last moment he reached past her, taking a glass from the shelf behind her head.

Turning on the tap with unnecessary violence, he filled it to overflowing and took a couple of deep swallows, the water still dripping from his fingers.

'So what happened, darling?' he said at last. 'You're not trying to claim that you fell hopelessly in love with me so that suddenly all the money ceased to matter? That all you cared about was me and nothing more?'

'Would you believe me if I said yes?'

She looked deep into those dark eyes as she spoke, willing him to believe her, wanting him to know that was just how it had been.

She saw the change in his expression, the flash of something deep in his eyes before they narrowed sharply. He made a slight movement of his head, putting the glass down again slowly, as if he was actually considering how to reply, and a weak flame of hope lit in her heart. Perhaps all was not lost. Perhaps...

'Aidan, please...'

Impulsively she reached out to take his hand, holding it tightly, willing him to believe what she was saying.

She was so sharply attuned to everything about him that she knew the exact moment that he made up his mind. She saw the subtle change, the flare of rejection in the ebony depths of his gaze, and it was like a bitter blow to her heart.

'No.'

It was clipped and brutal. The way that he eased his hand away from hers spoke more eloquently of his frame of mind than any more forceful gesture he might have used. He didn't even trouble to react strongly, but simply expressed his contempt by lifting her fingers from his as carelessly as if she had been some troublesome, clinging child who had worn out his patience once and for all.

'For a woman who claimed to be in love, you found a replacement for me pretty damn fast. So, frankly, my dear, I wouldn't believe a word you said.'

'Then it's just as well I didn't mean it, isn't it?'

She didn't know where she found the strength to drag up the retort and fling it in his face. She could barely hear her own voice through the buzzing in her ears, the pain of rejection in her mind. But uppermost in her thoughts was something else, a realisation so apocalyptic that it left her incapable of considering anything else.

She had asked if he would believe her if she said she had loved him. And that was how she had thought it too— *loved,* in the past, an emotion she had once felt but which had now been completely destroyed by his callous behaviour at their wedding.

But even as she had spoken she had known the truth. She had recognised it and been unable to deny it, however much she had wanted to.

Ever since Aidan's public rejection of her she had told herself that she hated him. And that hatred had given her the strength to get through.

Until his reappearance at the Grange had woken all those old feelings again. Just the sight of him had set all those sensations racing through her body, licking along her nerves like flames speeding through tinder.

She didn't hate him—because the only feeling she could ever have for Aidan Wolfe was the love that had knocked her off her feet in the first moment she had ever seen him so that she had never been able to regain her balance ever since. She knew that it was dangerous, that it was practically suicidal. If he knew, then he would be capable of taking advantage of the situation swiftly and heartlessly.

In a swift, panic-stricken rush, a new sense of self-preservation flooded through India, tightening her jaw and stiffening her spine. She had come perilously close to admitting how she felt, and to do so would be like handing him her heart.

As soon as it was in his possession, he would toss it aside in cruel scorn, not heeding or caring where it fell. He had done it once before, so what was there to stop him from doing it again?

So now she switched on a brilliant smile, praying that it concealed the way she was slowly dying inside.

'Just testing!' she trilled, right into his dark, set face. 'I wanted to be sure that there was no room for any misunderstanding between us. After all, I wouldn't want you to get the wrong impression.'

'You certainly wouldn't.' Aidan's voice was as grim and unyielding as the lines into which his features were drawn.

With a sense of shock, India registered that it was only now, when there could be no doubt at all about his frame of mind, that she could realise the difference between the bleak hostility of his eyes and some other feeling that had been in them only seconds before. She wouldn't be foolish enough to call it warmth, but it had been there, and now it was gone.

'So we're both agreed on that, then. And now, if you don't mind...'

The smile she switched on was pure glucose in its false sweetness. To judge from Aidan's swift frown, it didn't deceive him for a moment, emphasising rather than concealing the hard-won control she was imposing on her behaviour.

'It's time I put these on to cook, or no one will eat before nine tonight.'

He watched in stony silence as she filled a pan with water and set it on the stove to heat. India could almost feel the cold fire of his glare burning into the skin between her shoulderblades, and she had to force herself to concentrate on what she was doing, positioning the pan with over-meticulous care.

'So you're quite happy playing the field, are you?'

It was only because she had her back to him that she dared speak at all. If she had to look into his face, had to endure the brutal force of that inimical hostility any longer, she felt that she would shatter into tiny pieces on the floor.

'You enjoy it that way?'

A harsh sound that was a mixture of a curse and a growl was Aidan's only response. India told herself to take it as a form of agreement, and continued with carefully assumed lightness.

'And what about later?'

'Later?'

'I mean how long can you live up to this reputation as a—stud?' The word left a nasty taste in her mouth. 'How long do you think you can live that sort of lifestyle?'

'As long as it takes,' Aidan returned cryptically.

'That's hardly very responsible.'

'Oh, I take my responsibilities very seriously. In today's sexual climate, I'd have to be a damned bloody fool not to.'

That she could believe. Aidan never made any move that wasn't carefully thought out, the results of his actions calculated to the nth degree. Wasn't that how he'd planned his final rejection of her, so that it had the maximum, humiliating impact?

'So it's OK now, while you're only thirty-five...'

Having finished her task, she was now obliged to turn back to him, though, unable to look him in the face, she fixed her gaze on a point just behind his left shoulder. Even then, she still found it impossible to be unaware of the way that the cynically watchful expression on his face belied his apparently relaxed position, leaning against the sink, hands in his pockets.

'But one day you'll be older. What happens then, when you—when you're not able to...?'

'Pull the women?' Aidan inserted sardonically when she hesitated. 'I'll worry about that when it happens.'

'If you must put it so crudely!' India snapped, painfully aware of the fact that her hesitation had not been because she was trying to find the right words. Instead it had been an uncontrollable physical reaction to the way his posture drew attention to his narrow hips and long, powerful legs, the gleam of his glossy dark hair in the evening sun slanting through the window.

Of course he didn't need to worry, she reflected bitterly. Men like Aidan didn't lose their appeal as they grew older. If anything, a few lines or the odd grey hair probably helped, adding a distinguished touch of maturity to an already lethal impact.

'But you have to admit that the image of an elderly lecher with an airhead young enough to be his granddaughter on his arm isn't quite such an attractive one. And even if you don't find yourself trapped into a lonely old age, what about children?'

The last word came out almost as a squeak, her throat having dried on her again—but this time for a very different reason. The change in Aidan's eyes as she spoke had frankly terrified her. She almost felt that the force of his glare would shrivel her into a heap of dust right where she stood.

'What about them?' The apparently casual question didn't quite work. Aidan's tone was very much at odds with what she could read in his face.

'Don't you want kids?'

'I did once. Changed my mind.'

The throwaway delivery was more successful this time. Perhaps a few minutes before she might actually have believed in it. But she had seen the raw emotion in his eyes, caught the hard edge to his words, and as a result found it hard to be convinced by the impression he was trying to give her.

'But you—'

'That pan's about to boil over.'

Subject closed, no further discussion; he didn't have to say it. His feelings were clearly stamped into every inch of his body as he swiftly levered himself upright and moved to adjust the heat under the now boiling water.

You told me how much you wanted children, she had been about to say. At least two, possibly three, and as soon as possible. Hadn't she spent long hours day-dreaming about what those children would look like? Dark-haired boys or girls, physically a mixture of herself and Aidan. She had pictured them here, in this house where she had grown up, a home just made for a family.

Suddenly she desperately wanted to be left alone.

'Perhaps you'd tell Mum and Gary that it'll be ready in about ten minutes.'

She prayed that it didn't sound like a dismissal. She had tried to make it simply casual. But as she pushed an escaping strand of hair back behind her ear Aidan turned to face her and she froze, the action half-completed as she saw the look in his eyes.

'What is it? Have I got a smudge on my nose?'

Automatically her fingers went to check, stilling again as

Aidan shook his head silently, an unexpected smile curving his lips. There was no warmth in his face, but all the same that smile had her toes curling in response.

'No? Well, did you hear what I said?'

'Oh, yes, I heard.'

'Then...' Her voice trailed off as Aidan shook his head.

'In a minute.'

Low and husky, his voice sparked off a shivering trail of reaction as all the tiny hairs on her skin seemed to lift at the sound.

'But...'

'India, honey, I'll tell your mother anything you want in a minute, but there's something we have to put right first.'

India swallowed painfully.

'We do?'

Slowly Aidan nodded, and it was only when he reached out to take her hand, lifting it gently from her face, that she realised he had taken a couple of steps towards her, coming worryingly closer.

'You just don't look right,' he murmured, with an un-expected softness that only added to her confusion.

'I don't?'

She couldn't use her brain properly. It wouldn't concen-trate on his words, or the ones she wanted to use to answer him. Instead, it was fixed on the disturbingly pleasurable feeling of the warm strength of his fingers holding hers, the clean, male scent of his body so very close, the soft sound of his breathing.

'Not at all.'

Then, as she frowned her confusion, he smiled again, making her heart turn over in uncontrollable response.

'India, we've been here for almost an hour.'

His voice was slow and clear, as calm as if he were explaining a difficult concept to a none-too-bright child.

'And I'm sure your mother's been deliberately keeping tactfully well out of the way, leaving us alone together. We are supposed to be newly reconciled, but no one is going to believe that for a minute if you leave this kitchen looking the way you do now.'

India's frown deepened.

'The way…? How do you want me to look?'

She saw her mistake just a second too late, but that was time enough for Aidan. Already he had moved again, coming even nearer, his hands closing over her arms and pulling her towards him. Before she had time to collect her thoughts she was pressed up against him, the softness of her breasts crushed against the hard wall of his broad chest. She could feel the heat of his skin and the heavy thud of his heart through the fine cotton of his shirt.

'Like this,' he muttered huskily, and her own heart skipped several frantic beats as his dark head came down in a swift, swooping movement, capturing her lips in a fiercely demanding kiss.

Her head swam, her knees buckled beneath her, and she found herself clinging to his strength for support, her fingers closing desperately over his powerful shoulders, digging into the hard muscle she found there. She had no strength to fight when he deepened the kiss, forcing her lips apart, tormenting her mouth with his tongue, gently teasing at first, then building with a strong, primitive rhythm that drove her hazy thoughts onto unwanted paths.

It was impossible not to recall how that rhythm had once been employed by other, more intimate parts of his body. How that potent, pulsing movement had started slowly at first, then built and built into a raging, uncontrollable force that had exploded in such a crescendo of delight that simply remembering it made her head spin deliriously.

She had no idea whether long minutes had passed or simply seconds. All time, all awareness of her surroundings, faded from her mind and she knew only that Aidan was there, that she was in his arms, and it was the only place she wanted to be.

But then at last he raised his head, freeing her to draw

in a raw, gasping breath. She swayed slightly on her feet
as he released her.

'Now...'

For a second Aidan's own breathing was as uneven as
her own, but almost immediately he regained control over
it, looking down at her with a dark flame of triumph deep
in his eyes. India could only stare back, knowing that the
blood that had washed her face was ebbing rapidly, leaving
her cheeks pale under eyes that were wide and dark with
shock.

'*Now* you look just perfect. Now your mother won't need
to wonder what you've been doing. She'll only have to look
at your face to know exactly what we've been up to.'

His smile of triumph widened hatefully before, dropping
a final, brief kiss on the very tip of her nose, he turned on
his heel and strolled out of the room.

'It's *when,* not *if.*' Uncalled for, and totally unwanted,
Aidan's words of almost a week earlier slid into her head.
'It's as inevitable as the sun rising tomorrow morning, and
all I have to do is wait.'

And now, no matter how hard she tried to resist it, in
spite of all her attempts to push it from her mind, India
knew precisely why he had been so very sure of himself—
and of her.

Her reaction to that kiss had taught her, more clearly than
any words could possibly manage, just how much of an
effect Aidan Wolfe had on her. His brief caress had only
woken her physical appetites, leaving her hungry for more.

Her whole body still quivered in response to his touch,
aching in unfulfilled yearning, so that it was all she could
do to watch him go and still remain silent. Every nerve
seemed to scream at her to call him back, to be demanding
more of those wickedly seductive feelings, the pulsing excitement that set every bit of her alive with blazing desire.
She couldn't leave things so incomplete, and yet, for her
own safety, she knew that she had to.

Shaking her head in despair, India thought that for the

first time she really understood just how perfect a trap Aidan had created to ensnare her. No matter which way she turned, she could see no way out, no chance of escape.

If she stayed, the need for him she already felt could only grow stronger, more impossible to conceal with each day that passed. But if she succumbed to the physical yearning that had her in thrall, then she was putting herself even more completely into Aidan's power. She would lay herself open to even more hurt than ever before when, with his desire sated, he discarded her—as he inevitably would.

She had barely recovered from the pain of his last rejection of her. She couldn't face it happening again. But she couldn't leave either. There was her mother and Gary to consider, and, hopefully, her father. She couldn't let them all down now.

CHAPTER EIGHT

INDIA put the last container of food into the picnic basket and snapped the catches shut. Taking a step backwards, she gasped aloud in shock as the unthinking movement brought her hard up against a strong, muscular body.

'Steady.'

Amusement threaded through the deep tones as Aidan's hands came out to support her, restoring her uncertain balance. But even having both feet firmly back on the ground did nothing to ease the frantic racing of her heart that was the result of every nerve-end leaping into sensual awareness of his forceful and very physical presence.

'You startled me! Creeping up on me like that!'

'That's obvious.'

The dry humour had intensified now, and India felt the wash of colour in her cheeks deepening in response to it.

'You're as nervous as a cat. But I did not *creep*. Your thoughts must have been miles away for you not to have heard me.'

'I was concentrating.'

The look he slanted in her direction was frankly sceptical, that touch of humour still curling his sensual mouth, but all he said was, 'Is that it, then?'

He nodded towards the wicker basket on the kitchen table.

'Ready?'

India could only manage an unintelligible murmur. The truth was that 'ready' was the exact opposite of the way she was feeling. In fact, she doubted that she would ever feel mentally prepared for this.

'Right.' Obviously, Aidan had taken her response as agreement. 'I'll put this in the car, then.'

Swinging the basket off the table, he headed towards the door with it, leaving her with no option but to follow. Aidan clearly expected her to do just that, she reflected grimly. Her uneasy mood was in no way improved by the frowning glance he directed at her over his shoulder.

'You coming?'

'Do I have a choice?' India flung back at him, green eyes flashing defiance. 'I rather got the impression that I was to obey orders strictly. That I should jump when you snapped your fingers—*or else*!'

Aidan's smile mocked her indignation, incensing her further.

'I simply suggested that we should do things together.'

'*Suggested!*'

India gave a snort of disbelief, hating his exaggeratedly reasonable tone.

'"Suggested" is not the word I would use. It gives an impression of there being a possibility of refusal. What you said had more the character of an imperial decree. "It would look more convincing if we did things as a couple..."'

Deliberately she mimicked Aidan's words from when he had announced his plans for this outing.

'I was left in little doubt that disagreement was most definitely *not* on the cards.'

After his original suggestion that they look more convincing, he hadn't let the matter drop. He had mentioned it over dinner that evening, knowing only too well that her mother, believing in what she thought was a romantic reconciliation, would take his side in the matter. And this morning he had tracked her down to where she'd been putting fresh sheets on Gary's bed and delivered an ultimatum that had left no room for argument.

She'd tried to object even though she'd known she was fighting a losing battle.

'I don't have time to do anything else,' she declared, struggling to push the duvet into its navy cover. 'I have to be at the hospital. I know he's no longer in the deep coma, but my father needs me.'

'Not every minute of every day, he doesn't,' Aidan put in bluntly, taking the quilt from her and finishing the job with what India privately considered ostentatious speed and ease. 'Your mother's there all the time, and Gary too. And, besides, he's asleep more often than not. Your mother would want you to take some time off.'

'Perhaps.' India plumped up the pillows with unnecessary vigour, not prepared to let him know that her mother had in fact expressed the very same thought to her only that morning.

'She might even start to question whether this supposed reconciliation is all it's cracked up to be.'

'And you would hate to disillusion her.'

She tried not to show the shiver that crept over her skin at seeing the way his eyes darkened in anger at her obvious sarcasm. But a moment later he had shrugged off her hostility with supreme indifference.

'I don't think you would want me to burden her with the whole truth—not yet, anyway,' he murmured with a dangerous edge to the words. 'After all, your father isn't exactly out of the woods, even if he has improved noticeably.'

He had her in a cleft stick there. There was no denying the improvement in her father's condition since those first dark days, but he still drifted in and out of consciousness, unable to register much. He couldn't speak either; such words as he could manage being blurred and unintelligible.

He was also still in blissful ignorance as to Aidan's presence at the Grange. Using his opposition to her marriage the year before to support her argument, India had managed to persuade both her mother and Gary that it was better not to tell him even that Aidan had come back to Westbury until he was stronger. She was afraid even to contemplate the possible setback that might result if he knew that the man to whom he had pledged his house was now in residence.

'So what's it to be?'

Aidan sounded supremely casual. Listening to him, no one would ever have believed that he had just hinted at the sort of threat that could quite possibly bring her whole world crashing down about her ears.

'I suppose…'

He gave a nod of grim satisfaction, not troubling himself with the fact that she hadn't actually *agreed*. He knew that she had no other possible choice.

'How about a film, or a meal?'

India struggled not to let her pain show in her face. They had shared too many meals in restaurants together in the past, and the thought of sitting close to him in the intimate darkness of a cinema was not something she could contemplate with any degree of equanimity.

'No?' He read her feelings in her face. 'Then the theatre? A race meeting? Somewhere you can wear those designer clothes you so love.'

That brought her head up sharply, her eyes wide with amazement.

'Designer clothes! You've got to be joking. Everything I wear is either handmade from scratch or cut down from something in my mother's wardrobe. If you don't believe me,' she went on in response to his change of expression, 'then I'll show you. You can go through my wardrobe with a fine-tooth comb and you won't find a single designer label. I can guarantee that!'

'There's no need for that.' The words were surprisingly uneven. 'It's just… You're very good.'

'I enjoy it.'

Why did she get the impression that he had been about to say something very different but had changed his mind at the last minute?

'I always thought I'd like to do it professionally— maybe even design. But I decided that I'd better do something rather more practical, something that would mean I could contribute to the family budget as soon as possible after I left school. A secretarial course seemed much more sensible. The dressmaking became just a hobby and a practical way of extending what would otherwise have been a very limited wardrobe. I even made—'

'You even made...?' Aidan prompted, when a sudden stab of unhappiness made her choke the words off hastily.

'My wedding dress, if you must know,' India muttered unwillingly.

'But it was so beautiful.'

'I didn't think you'd noticed. You were too busy looking forward to saying your big line.'

'I wasn't *looking forward* to it.' Flames of anger flared in the darkness of his eyes, and she knew she'd overstepped the mark dangerously.

'Well, thank you for the compliment anyway.' Bitterness darkened her attempt at flippancy. 'I'm glad to know that my efforts weren't completely wasted.'

'You looked wonderful, Princess. I'd never seen anything as lovely as you were, walking down that aisle towards me. Any man would have been proud to have you as his bride.'

'But not you!' The pain was stronger now, making her words as bleak and cold as an arctic sea. 'Obviously you're not just "any man".'

Knowing she would break down if he said anything more about the day they should have been married, she muttered something about seeing to her mother's bed next, and fled. To her horror, Aidan followed silently and once more set about helping her, stripping the bed with brisk efficiency. He was obviously not going to leave her alone until he got an answer.

'You're very good at this,' India said in some surprise. 'You must have had plenty of practice.'

'I used to help my mother when my father was—away.'

'How old were you then?'

'Seven or eight.' Those dark eyes looked strangely clouded. 'I've always thought that fresh, clean sheets are one of the simplest luxuries in life.'

'Me too.'

The thought of Aidan as a small boy, helping his mother make the beds, was so poignant that it twisted sharply in her heart and she couldn't hold back a faint sigh in response. Hearing it, Aidan straightened up from stretching the sheet over the bed.

'You need a break, India,' he said unexpectedly, misinterpreting the reason for her behaviour. 'You look tired, worn out with holding your family together since your father became ill. You've cooked, cleaned, run—'

'Someone had to do it!'

She wasn't going to admit to the sleepless nights she had endured since he had come back into her life. She had spent so many long hours lying awake in the darkness, fearful of the sleep that brought long, erotic dreams of Aidan interspersed with sharper, more painful replaying of happy times they had shared in their brief courtship. She didn't know which of them was worse—only that each devastated her with its unique sense of loss when she finally awoke.

'And you took it on so that your mother would be free to be at the hospital. But now you need some time for yourself. You've been under strain, too. Your father's going to be OK, India...'

His unexpected gentleness was more than India could take. Hot tears burned in her eyes and she swung away, turning her back on him in order to hide them.

'India!'

She heard his swift movement, sensed the moment he came close to her. What she wasn't prepared for was the way his arms came round her, their warmth and strength infinitely comforting. It was impossible to resist the urge to lean back against him, feeling the hardness of his body supporting her.

Her head fitted against his shoulder as it had done in the

past, his cheek resting against her hair. It felt like coming home.

'I—thought he was going to die,' she choked. 'I was afraid I'd lost him for ever.'

'I know.' Aidan's voice was low, rough-edged, his breath softly stirring her hair. 'But he's going to pull through— you must believe that.'

Slowly he turned her in his arms, one hand coming up to brush the tear stains from her face with a touch so soft, so delicate, it seemed almost shocking when contrasted with his size and strength.

'Your father's a very lucky man. He has the three of you worrying about him, willing him to get well—and he must know that.'

Slowly India nodded. But a new and very disturbing thought had entered her mind, distracting her even from the physical pleasure of being in Aidan's arms in this very different, very gentle way. There had been an odd note in his voice, one that linked his words to her memories of that day in the attic.

'Aidan, how did you feel when your father...?'

'When he died?' Aidan finished for her when her throat closed over the word. 'To be perfectly honest, I felt free.'

'*Free!*' India echoed, horrified. 'That's a dreadful thing to say! I can't believe...'

'Believe it!' Aidan declared indifferently. 'You asked how I felt—I told you.'

But his eyes were black pools of hostility, the mood of seconds before totally destroyed. Abruptly she was released, and he collected the discarded bedlinen, bundling it up into his arms, obviously heading for the door.

India couldn't let him go like that. Those few seconds in his arms had affected her deeply and she still hadn't recovered from their impact.

'About this outing you're so set on—I don't want you spending money on me. If we have to do anything, I'd rather it was something simple. Something that doesn't cost anything.'

'In that case we might as well just go for a walk.'

Aidan's sardonic intonation made it plain that his suggestion wasn't meant to be taken seriously, but India pounced on it thankfully.

'That's it. Perfect! I can't think of anything I'd like better. In fact, why don't we make it a picnic—a full day outing?'

She didn't know why she had added that last remark, only that it had suddenly seemed important to get away from the emotive surroundings of the Grange with its echoes of the past. Perhaps in more neutral surroundings they had a chance of if not exactly making peace at least coming to some sort of compromise that would make living together easier in the future.

'I'm surprised you agreed to go along with this,' India said now as she followed Aidan out to the car. 'I mean, you'd never have done anything similar when we knew each other before.'

'Probably not,' Aidan returned with infuriating equanimity. He didn't even trouble to turn and look at her. 'Perhaps you should ask yourself why that is.'

'You're not trying to claim that I...?'

Her voice trailed off as she recalled that in those first few weeks of knowing him he had taken her to the most fashionable and expensive restaurants, the newest shows. She had had the best that money could buy, and she had never raised a word of protest.

The truth was that she had been afraid to. She had been scared that if she had admitted to her preference for the more simple things Aidan, being the worldly sophisticate he was, would find her naive and uninteresting. If she bored him, she feared she might lose him, that he might turn to someone more like himself, like the women with whom his name had been linked in the past.

Later, when he had asked her to marry him, she had

relaxed. They would have all the time in the world to get to know each other now, she had thought. How wrong she had been!

'Are you saying that if I'd suggested this sort of thing when we first met you'd have agreed?' she demanded sharply.

'And are you saying that you'd have chosen something as simple as this in preference to the things I offered?' Aidan countered harshly, swinging round abruptly, the cold light in his eyes telling her he wouldn't believe a word she said if she did reply. 'Don't tell me you have depths I didn't guess at.'

'Depths you didn't even try to find out about!'

'Which brings us back to pots and kettles, I think,' Aidan retorted. 'We were fools ever to think we could make marriage work, Princess. We never even knew each other at all.'

'Except that you never even planned to try and make it work!' India flung at him, using anger to conceal her pain. 'After all, you were just deceiving me about everything from the start.'

'Not everything, darling,' he stunned her by drawling. 'And certainly not right from the start.'

The gleam in his dark eyes left her in little doubt as to exactly what was in his mind, and the heat that had bathed her face spread all over her body, making her skin glow pink under the white sleeveless vest top she wore with emerald-green shorts.

She had left her black hair hanging casually loose, but now she scooped it up off the back of her neck, twisting a blue and green floral scarf around the hasty ponytail, too hot with embarrassment under his scrutiny to bear the feel of the hair against her skin.

'But I admit that in the past I gave you what I thought you wanted. If you would have preferred something different, you had only to say. Or, rather, I should have asked.'

Which left her gaping like a stranded fish, pushed right back into the uncomfortable mood of moments before.

'Are you trying to back out of this, Princess?'

'Oh, no,' she assured him hastily. 'In fact I've been looking forward to it. We could go down by the river, if you like. I've packed some stale bread so we can feed the ducks, and…'

Her voice trailed off as she saw the expression on his face. He was looking at her as if he had never seen her before in his life.

'I want to come, Aidan,' she finished softly, and saw him blink hard, just once, as if in confusion.

'Right, we'll be off, then.'

As she fastened her seatbelt he slid into the driver's seat beside her, and suddenly India was forced to wonder if 'looking forward to it' was anything like an accurate description of just how she was feeling.

She was tantalisingly on edge, acutely sensitive to every movement of his strong, lean body, the firm, decisive actions of his hands on the wheel or the gear lever. The breeze from the open window blew his black hair back from his face, tangling it in soft disarray across his wide forehead.

She longed to touch him, wanted to reach out and run her fingertips over the worn denim that covered his thigh, feel the power of muscle beneath the coarse material as his feet moved on the pedals. She wanted to rest her head against the hard strength of his shoulder, inhale the intensely personal, intimate scent that was his alone, feel his warmth, hear his heart beat in forceful unison with hers. Every inch of her body was gripped with a singing tension that had her shifting uneasily in her seat.

'Too much breeze for you?'

Aidan had caught her unsettled movement, and now he slanted an enquiring glance in her direction.

'I— Oh, no, I'm fine.'

But the small interruption had been enough to bring her up hard against the wanton eroticism of her thoughts, mak-

ing her realise just what a dangerous path had opened up
before her.

What *was* she doing? Wasn't this what had happened to
her before?

A year ago, foolishly, unthinkingly at the mercy of her
most primitive sensual instincts, she had been unable to
think clearly or logically. She had fallen head over heels
into his trap and into his bed without a thought for her own
safety. Was she going to let herself be caught that way
again, heedless of the consequences?

At least this time she knew more of the real truth behind
Aidan's actions. She understood his motives far more
clearly, all of which should make her have second or even
third thoughts about the way she was feeling, but...

'Your mother seemed so happy this morning.' Aidan's
voice broke into her thoughts, dragging her back to the
present with a jolt. 'The news from the hospital has really
bucked her up.'

'She's pleased that Dad's made such good progress.'
Genuine happiness gave India's reply the lift it needed so
as not to betray the worrying tenor of her thoughts.
'They're even talking of moving him out of Intensive Care
now and onto a normal ward. Of course, his speech is still
a problem, but when...'

'What is it?'

Aidan had caught the way her breath had hissed through
her teeth as she faced up to a new quandary.

'You were thinking of your father,' he went on when she
couldn't answer him. 'Wondering what will happen when
he's well enough to be discharged.'

India could only stare at him in bewilderment. How had
he known so exactly what she was thinking? Had her
thoughts shown so clearly in her face, or was he some sort
of a mind-reader?

'You needn't worry.' Aidan spoke quietly, his attention
apparently fixed on the road ahead. 'Obviously he'll come
back to the Grange to convalesce.'

It wasn't obvious to India at all.

'You can't mean that. You wouldn't want him there.'

'I'll agree that I don't exactly anticipate *enjoying* his company,' Aidan returned drily. 'And I'm sure that he won't want mine. But I told you, Princess, I'm a reasonable man. Your father owed me a lot of money, but now I have the Grange in payment of that debt—which, incidentally, I much prefer to the cash. The least I can do is offer him a roof over his head until he's well enough to find one for himself.'

'You'd do that?' India couldn't believe what she was hearing.

Aidan nodded, keeping his eyes fixed on the road ahead.

'Our arrangement could continue exactly as before. After all, unless you and I are working on our relationship, your father could easily fear that I am on the point of taking over the Grange, and I don't think he'll feel up to moving from the family home in the near future.'

So once again the price was her agreement to play the part of his reconciled fiancée. He knew she would agree. She had no possible alternative. But she still couldn't even begin to see what Aidan might get out of it. Why not move them out and have done with it?

What was really going on in that dark, devious mind? Were the plans he had let her see simply the tip of the iceberg, with three-quarters of what was yet to come still hidden from sight?

She had believed that she had gone a long way towards fulfilling the demands Aidan had made, that pretty soon she might actually begin to see light at that end of the tunnel. But what if, far from being close to the end of this nightmare, she was in fact still very much at the beginning? What if she had only just started to learn exactly what it was Aidan wanted from her?

CHAPTER NINE

'SOMETHING bothering you, Princess?'

The lightness of Aidan's tone had India gritting her teeth against an angry retort. She had no doubt that he suspected exactly what was on her mind.

'I was wondering how you will explain away all the work you've planned for the house. My father will know that the time's run out on his IOUs. He'll never believe that you'd put your money into the Grange just for the fun of it.'

'He'll believe it if he thinks I might yet be his son-in-law.'

Aidan's words made India suddenly sit upright in her seat, an uncomfortable memory fretting at her mind.

That week they had spent together with her parents away had come at the end of a difficult time. A time when Aidan had suddenly seemed distant and preoccupied, spending more time in London than he did with her. When she had finally tackled him about it, he had admitted that it hadn't just been work that had kept him away.

'I needed time on my own—to get my thoughts together.'

'Thoughts about what?' she had asked, suddenly fearful that he had changed his mind, that he didn't want to marry her at all.

'About us. Look, Princess, we've come so far so fast. Are you sure this is really what you want?'

'Of course it is!' Her protest had been high and sharp, still touched with that edge of fear.

'Are you sure you're not staging some sort of rebellion? After all, you've always been your father's little princess, and now...'

115

'No, Aidan. It isn't like that at all. Look, if this is just because of the way my dad's been behaving, then you needn't worry. And anyway, if you want to know how to get round him, then I have the perfect solution. All you have to do is to offer to help pay for the restorations for the Grange.'

But Aidan had shaken his head, adamantly refusing even to consider the suggestion.

'If you buy someone's approval in that way, how do you ever know whether you're wanted for yourself or for what you could give them?'

'But you will live at the Grange in the end, won't you?' Coming back to the present, a sense of unease made India's voice edgy. 'After all, having invested so much in the house, you wouldn't want to let anyone else have it.'

Aidan concentrated on negotiating a particularly tricky turn before he replied.

'Don't you think your father would hate to see the Marchant family home in the hands of someone he's always disapproved of?'

'Perhaps,' India said slowly. 'On the other hand, when he sees what you've planned for the house—how you saved it from ruin, planning improvements that will bring the old place into the twentieth century but won't damage its character in any way—he might actually admit to himself that it was his fault it got that way in the first place. He might be able to see that the Grange is now in the hands of someone who loves it as much as he always did. And, if he can swallow some of his foolish pride, he might just see that perhaps he was never really the right person to be in charge of it.'

'Do you really think that's possible?' Aidan sounded frankly sceptical.

'I hope so. Dad's made rather a mess of things, to say the least. I can only pray that when he recovers from this illness he'll realise where he went wrong and start to put his life back together again.'

Suddenly becoming aware of his dark eyes on her face, the thoughtful, considering expression in them, she frowned nervously.

'Why are you looking at me like that?'

'Just thinking.' Aidan turned his attention back to the road. 'Some people might think you had cause to resent your father. After all, it was his foolishness that put you and your family in this difficult position.'

'I know. And, believe me, if he was well enough I'd want to shake him for being so stupid. But he's my father, and in spite of all his faults I still love him.'

'And so does your mother.' There was a strange intonation on the statement, one India couldn't even begin to interpret.

'Of course she does! He's her husband!'

The sudden, totally uncharacteristic crashing of the gears brought her eyes to his face in a rush, seeing the unexpected tension that drew his skin tight across his harsh bone structure.

'Aidan?'

'It's not a given, India.' The bleakness of his voice matched his expression, worrying her. 'A wedding ring doesn't mean happy ever after. Sometimes all that a marriage does is paper over the cracks.'

'You sound as if you're speaking from experience.'

India spoke carefully. The rough way that Aidan had flung the words at her revealed intense personal feeling, but she didn't know if he would allow any further questioning on the matter.

In the past, the few times he had ever spoken of his parents he had also made it plain that he would not welcome any further questions on the matter. Then, fearful of doing anything to upset him, she had kept silent. But she was unable to do that now, even if pursuing the subject would be like setting light to the fuse on a powerful bomb.

'You know about such things?'

'From the inside.' Aidan nodded grimly. 'And how. My

parents didn't have a marriage, they had their own, private civil war. They tore each other to pieces almost daily. Neither of them could be faithful to anyone for a second, and I grew up with them parading a series of what they euphemistically termed "friends" in front of me. I barely had time to learn any of their names before there was a new one in their place.'

'Why didn't they split up?' India's shock showed in her voice. She had never guessed at any of this.

'Oh, they did, frequently, but never for long. My father was always moving out, but he usually came back pretty quickly. The trouble was that they couldn't live apart, but neither could they live together—and they made life hell for everyone around them.'

Including their son, India thought privately, her heart aching for the child he had been then, whose unhappiness was hidden now behind the flat, matter-of-fact speech of the man.

'It's an old story. They weren't the first, and I doubt very much they'll be the last.'

India longed desperately to be able to reach out to Aidan and just hold him tight, but she knew he would violently reject any such gesture.

'It wasn't a love match, or even a love-hate relationship. More like a lust-hate relationship. They turned their lives into one long battle. They fought all the time—great screaming matches that often developed into actual violence. In the end they killed each other.'

'Aidan, no!'

This time she couldn't hold back. Impulsively India's hand moved to rest on Aidan's arm, trying to convey silent sympathy, her green eyes wide and dark with shock. Aidan glanced at her briefly before turning his attention back to the road, his mouth twisting bitterly.

'Oh, not literally, perhaps. But as near as damn it. They had just had the latest in a long line of so-called "reconciliations"...'

His laugh was hard and brittle, seeming to splinter the air inside the car.

'They started to argue again even on the way home from the hotel where my father had been staying and my mother had driven to pick him up. It was the middle of winter, a freezing night, but they were fighting so hard that they didn't see the ice until it was too late. They went right across the motorway and into the path of an oncoming lorry. They were both killed immediately.'

'But how do you know they were fighting? It could just have been an—'

'I *know*,' Aidan cut in harshly. 'I was in the back of the car. It was a miracle that I wasn't killed as well.'

He fell into a taut, brooding silence that India did not dare to break. 'I never let anyone else drive me,' he had once said, when she had offered to take the wheel, and now she understood why. Oh, God, she understood so well that it made her blood run cold just to think of it.

At long last he stirred again, raking one hand through the ebony darkness of his hair with a deep sigh.

'They buried them together.' Once more that harsh, cynical laugh made her wince. 'It was perhaps the closest they'd ever been in their lives.'

'Except for when you were conceived,' India ventured.

'Hardly.' The grim humour in his voice was even worse than that laugh had been.

'But in order to make love—'

She broke off sharply as his dark head moved in vehement denial.

'Oh, they could *have sex* anywhere, any time—no problem. Even when they detested the other, and wished them dead, they still fancied the pants off each other. Lust doesn't need emotions. You don't have to have love for it, that's for sure. It isn't an essential ingredient for brilliant sex. That can even be fired by hate.'

'Like you and me?'

It came out shakily, with a revealing break in the middle.

Aidan waited until he had turned the car off the road and onto a rough patch of ground that served as a makeshift parking space before shutting off the engine and turning to face her.

'Oh, Princess,' he said into the sudden, deep silence. 'I never *hated* you.'

His eyes were so dark they were almost black, and she could read nothing of his thoughts in them. His body language gave nothing away either, his lean, powerful frame apparently perfectly relaxed in his seat, his hands loose on the wheel.

He was giving her no signals, nothing she could pick up on in order to be able to understand just what lay behind what he had said. 'I never *hated* you'. But what *had* he felt?

Aidan pushed open his door and made a move as if to get out, but then suddenly swung back to face her.

'You know,' he continued softly, 'there's one thing that puzzles me. I've been back—what, about a week now?—in your house and in your life. And yet in all that time never once have you asked me *why* I walked out on you.'

Hot anger unfroze India's mouth, freeing her tongue so that she could speak at last.

'That's because it's blatantly obvious!'

'Is it?'

Something in his expression, some small change that she couldn't quite define, made her look at him more closely. But as soon as she focused on him it was to find that the tiny, elusive betrayal of his inner feelings had gone, leaving his face as bleakly inscrutable as before.

'If it isn't,' she said slowly, 'then tell me...'

'No,' Aidan countered harshly. 'You tell me.'

'Why? Well, obviously you did it because...'

Denied the escape route of the single word 'hate' that had sustained her for so long, she floundered awkwardly, looking for a possible alternative.

'Because I offended your male pride by wanting your money rather than just you—'

'If you truly think that, India,' Aidan inserted, his words strangely flat, 'then you really didn't know me at all.'

And, leaving her gasping in shock and confusion, he pushed open the car door roughly, getting out and moving to open the boot, then lifting out the picnic basket.

'Now, just a minute!'

Scrambling out of the car after him, India hurried to his side.

'You can't just make a declaration like that and then leave it!'

His only response was an indifferent shrug of his broad shoulders before he slammed the boot shut and set off down the narrow path that led to the riverbank.

'Aidan!'

She almost had to trot in order to keep up with the long, swift strides that covered the ground so quickly.

'May I remind you that you were the one who walked out on me?'

'So I did.' He sounded almost amused, his words laced with darkly cynical humour. 'But I was also the one who asked you to marry me. Have you ever considered that if I'd really wanted to hurt you it would have been far crueller to have gone ahead and married you, tied you to a life with me?'

'Tied…?'

Confusion stopped her dead in her tracks, but Aidan kept on walking. His head was held high, his long back stiffly erect, his face determinedly turned away from her.

'Aidan!'

This time she had to run to catch him up, and she only managed to do so because he stopped so suddenly that she almost ran into him.

'This looks like a good spot for the picnic,' he said as she struggled to catch her breath. 'What do you think?'

Unable to believe his casual tone, India barely spared the

secluded dell a glance. She registered the fact that the cluster of bushes provided almost total privacy, as well as pleasant shade from the heat of the sun, and that the river tumbled down over a mini-waterfall, sparkling in the light before creating a wide, fairly deep pool a short distance away.

'It's perfect,' she managed abstractedly, before returning to the matter that was uppermost in her mind. 'Why do you keep avoiding giving me any answers…?'

'I'm not avoiding anything,' Aidan returned sharply. 'If you ask the right questions, I'll answer.'

'The right questions…'

India actually shook her head in confusion. What *were* the right questions?

'Fine.' The curtness of the single syllable told her that Aidan had interpreted her reaction as a refusal to say anything more. 'So, do you want to eat now?'

He busied himself with unfolding and spreading out the tartan rug they had brought with them before sprawling on it lazily, stretching his long legs out comfortably as he began to unpack the picnic basket.

After a couple of very necessary seconds to collect her thoughts and compose herself, India joined him on the grass. The rest of the unpacking was completed in silence, and it was only when they both had food on their plates and Aidan had poured a glass of wine that she found the strength to try again.

'When you asked me to marry you, was your proposal just part of your plan? I mean, did you ask me simply in order to—to—?'

She couldn't say the words 'to hurt me', not wanting to give so much away.

'To be able to humiliate me by rejecting me at the wedding?'

Aidan took his time about responding. He finished a mouthful of cold chicken, washing it down with a swallow of wine before he spoke.

'Believe it or not, I hadn't meant things to work out like that. I actually turned up at the church meaning to marry you.'

It was the last thing she had expected, and it made her thoughts whirl so violently that she had to set down her glass rather suddenly for fear that she might spill it.

'Oh, come on! You don't expect me to believe that?'

Aidan's dark eyes met her sceptical green ones over the top of his glass.

'Why not? It happens to be true. At the time I really thought I could go through with it.'

'Go through with it!'

India was grateful for the outrage that masked her pain. She had known he had never loved her, but, all the same, nothing had prepared her for the bluntness of this declaration.

'You make marriage sound like some form of appalling torture.'

'You certainly came far too expensive,' Aidan replied. 'The return on my investment was way below what I'd hoped for.'

'Your *investment*! It wasn't some bloody business deal!'

'Wasn't it? So, tell me, what made the difference? You wanted me and my money, and I wanted you. All we had to do was to arrange the terms.'

'You're not claiming you didn't get what you wanted?'

'Not enough,' Aidan stated ambiguously, not making it plain in what way he had not got as much as he had desired. 'But you were the one who made it plain that you wanted marriage and you wanted it *fast*.'

'Don't remind me!'

Staring sightlessly down at the rug, India traced the lines of the pattern with a finger. She didn't want to recall how—out of her mind with love for this man—she had only wanted to have his ring on her finger and hadn't cared about anything else.

A sudden thought struck home to her, stilling the restless movement of her hand.

'And what did you want from me, apart from the obvious?'

She froze as one of his strong hands closed over hers, the other sliding under her chin, lifting her face to meet his cold-eyed scrutiny.

'Don't sell yourself short, Princess,' he murmured softly. 'You have one hell of a lot going for you even apart from the way you look. You have style, cachet, status. You are one very classy lady.'

He actually meant it as a compliment, India realised dazedly. He really believed that she would be *flattered* by what he had said. In the back of her mind she could hear her father's voice repeating the accusation that she had rejected so vehemently just over a year before.

When she had derided his belief that Aidan had only mercenary reasons for wanting to marry her, her father had added something else, something far less easy to refute.

'But there's one thing no amount of money can buy, Indy, love—and that's status. Aidan Wolfe may have made a fortune, but he's dragged himself up from nowhere. You are a Marchant of Westbury Grange. Our ancestry goes back to the Normans, and that's something he can't lay claim to. With you at his side, Aidan Wolfe would have entrée to some of the most prestigious homes and events in the country, places that his millions couldn't buy him into.'

She had laughed at the idea then—but now, with Aidan's use of that emotive word 'status', it had once more taken root in her mind. She could see how he might want that sort of social clout, how important it would be to him. It would be the one thing he couldn't get for himself.

'After all, you are the Lady of the Grange.'

The drawled comment was positively the last straw, driving her to wrench herself away from him, emerald eyes blazing rejection.

'Don't touch me! I don't want you anywhere near me!'

Anger drove her to her feet, glaring down at him, her anger fuelled by his coolly impassive expression.

'Because I'll tell you something, Mr Return-on-My-Investment Wolfe! I've never ceased to be grateful to you for the way you behaved a year ago! Oh, I know I didn't show it at the time, but when I calmed down I realised that you had done me a great favour by not marrying me. You set me free.'

'So that you could turn your attentions to Jim.'

'Jim?'

For a couple of seconds India couldn't remember that she had claimed Jim as the new man in her life, but then realisation dawned and she nodded her head emphatically.

'Yes, Jim! He's worth two of you—in character if not in financial terms.'

'And of course character is much more important to you than money *now*.'

'What?' India frowned her confusion, not understanding the emphasis on that last word. 'I'd like you to explain that.'

'Surely I don't have to? If you really know as little as you claim, why don't you ask your father—or your bank manager?'

'I can't— My bank manager?'

'Oh, come on, Princess! You're not trying to pretend ignorance of the pre-nuptial agreement?'

'Pre… What pre-nuptial agreement?'

'The one you got your father to negotiate for you. The little matter of a small fortune invested in an account in your name, whether we married or not.'

'Oh, now I know you're making all this up! For one thing, no one would ever sign away money on terms like that, least of all you! And, for another, if this mythical money really is mine, then why haven't I seen a trace of it? There hasn't even been a bank statement—nothing!'

'Do you think I'd let you get your greedy little hands on it straight away?' The cynicism of Aidan's tone was brutal in its cruelty. 'I had my lawyers tie it up so that you couldn't touch it for a year. But you should have had notification on your birthday.'

But on her birthday she had been too caught up in the worries and problems that had resulted from her father's illness to even consider opening anything but the most essential post. There was a large bundle of letters in her room, still waiting for her attention.

'I didn't know. And I never—'

But Aidan seemed to have lost all interest in the subject, leaning back against the gnarled trunk of the tree and closing his eyes in rejection of her.

'And you're completely wrong,' he went on in a very different tone. 'Jim isn't the man for you. He's too much of a wimp.'

'You've no right—' India began indignantly, but broke off abruptly as those heavy lids lifted swiftly, dark eyes subjecting her to an insolent survey that made her skin crawl.

'Well, look at it this way—I've been at the Grange for what? A week now? And the man's never even put in an appearance. Hardly the action of a knight on a white charger when faced with a rival for his lady's hand.'

Which was not in the least surprising, considering the fact that Jim didn't even know she was taking his name in vain like this.

'That's because he's well aware of the fact that you're not a *rival*!' she declared, with what she hoped sounded like more conviction than she was actually feeling. 'He knows that I'm not interested in anyone else.'

'Is that a fact?' Aidan's sceptical tone and his lifted eyebrow questioned the truth of her declaration. 'And here I was, thinking that it was cowardice that was keeping him away. It's a strange relationship, though. You claim he's the love of your life—and yet you never see him. You've been at home every night when you haven't been at the hospital.'

'That's none of your business!' India exploded, fearful of how close he was getting to the truth. 'You might have taken possession of the Grange, but you don't own me! I'll do as I want, when I want, and I'll thank you to keep out of my life!'

There was no response from the man before her, his silence stirring her anger so that she knew she had to get away now or do something truly dreadful.

'And right now what I want is to go for a walk *alone*!'

The forceful emphasis on the last word fell disappointingly flat when Aidan made no attempt to stop her, not even reacting to her declaration of defiance. Instead, he adjusted his position against the trunk, relaxing as he got comfortable.

'See you,' he murmured, and closed his eyes again, leaving her with no option but to walk away, fuming with impotent rage as she headed off down the path.

CHAPTER TEN

ANGER drove India's feet forward in a headlong rush that expressed the blind fury building up inside her. She didn't care where she was going, simply marching along beside the river, kicking stones out of her way and wishing they were Aidan as she booted them hard with her toes.

How dared he? How dared he treat her like this? He had moved into her home, into her life, taken it over and...

And what?

The question threw itself at her, stopping her dead. Wasn't the truth that since Aidan's arrival she had been fighting so hard that she had never actually paused to consider just what she was fighting *against*?

All right, so Aidan had moved into the Grange—but then he had every legal right to do so. It was her father's fault he was there. *He* had been the one who had gambled away their family home so foolishly, the one who had risked everything, heedless of possible repercussions for his family.

Aidan, on the other hand, had been the one who had ensured that they had a roof over their heads when they needed it most. And, what was more, he had set in motion the vital repairs that had ensured the old house wouldn't fall into rack and ruin.

He had even asked her opinion about the work, carefully taking into account her preferences. He had also protected her mother from the unsavoury truth about her husband's behaviour, and by doing so had saved her father from some of the possible consequences of his actions.

But *why*?

And was it possible that the story of the pre-nuptial

agreement was true? She had to admit that it sounded like just the sort of opportunistic move her father might have made. It would certainly explain his gambling, if he had believed that her money would bail him out.

And... India came to a sudden halt, as if her thoughts were actually a wall that she had suddenly come up hard against. The timing would fit with that week when Aidan had been so distant, the time when he had said that he'd needed to get his thoughts together. What if it had been her apparent demands—seemingly relayed through her father— that had made him stop and reconsider?

And it would explain the cryptic, derogatory remarks Aidan had made about money since his reappearance in her life—and even before.

'You'll have to make do with what you've got; I have nothing more to give you,' he had flung at her in the church before he had finally walked away from her.

What if, all this time, there had been money—if not enough to pay her father's debts, then at least sufficient to make life considerably easier for them? And, if there was, it had come from Aidan.

So why would he ever have signed such a punitive pre-nuptial agreement? Particularly when he'd had no intention of going through with the marriage, and so not getting any-thing out of the deal?

'If you ask the right questions, I'll answer them.'

Aidan's voice sounded inside her head, making her frown in confusion. Just what *were* the right questions? How could she ask him if she didn't know what to say?

And then, from further back in her memory, from the time before Aidan had even proposed to her, there came another image—one that made her frown deepen.

She had been visiting Aidan in London, and had called in at his office there. Sitting at his desk, waiting for him to finish with some meeting or other, she had scribbled her name over and over on the headed notepaper, substituting

India Wolfe for India Marchant until a thought had struck her.

'Do you know,' she said impulsively when Aidan returned, 'Our names are made up of almost identical letters? AIDAN. INDIA. It must be fate!'

'Ah, yes, but…'

Coming to her side, he had taken the pen from her grasp.

'I think you'll find that you have one awkward little extra letter.'

With a firm, slashing stroke of the pen, he encircled the second 'I' in her name, isolating it from the other letters.

'Rather significant, don't you think?'

At the time she hadn't really understood just what he was implying. But now, with the scene replaying inside her head, taken in conjunction with the new facts she had learned so recently, she saw that extra letter taking on a more ominous significance.

I. I. I.

Suddenly she whirled round, heading back the way she had come. She was going to talk to Aidan and find the right questions to ask if it killed her!

It was something of a shock when she glanced at her watch and found that she had been away for almost an hour. Aidan must be wondering where she was.

He was doing nothing of the sort. When she arrived back at the little clearing, India could only stand and stare at the sight of Aidan still comfortably propped up against the tree. His eyes were firmly closed and he was obviously deeply, contentedly asleep.

The sight drove all her earlier questions and concerns completely from her mind. Moving quietly across the springy grass, she sank down beside him, curling her legs under her, her eyes fixed on his face.

'Aidan…' she said softly, but he didn't stir.

She was so close to him that she could hear the soft sound of his breathing, see the way his chest rose and fell. She could even catch the occasional flicker of the long, thick eyelashes that lay like black crescents above the hard line of his cheekbones. The sunlight warmed his tanned skin to a golden glow. Overhead, the leaves cast dappled shadows in a changing, shifting pattern on his face and clothes.

She had never seen him like this before, India realised with a little jolt of shock. Never once, even in the time that she had been engaged to him, had he ever fallen asleep in her presence. He might have slept in the same bed, but always after she had surrendered to exhaustion. And he had been wide awake and alert before she had surfaced in the mornings.

She might have shared his life, his bed, his body, but this particular intimacy was one he had always held back from her. Even in the aftermath of passion he had never succumbed to this very human weakness.

So had he never really trusted her completely?

Because, seeing how sleep transformed him, India couldn't help wondering if this was why he had held aloof. Did he know, or at least suspect, the way that this total relaxation would soften the hard lines of his face, giving him a younger, much more vulnerable appearance? Did he guess that it would wipe away the self-assured expression he wore like a mask in which to face the world?

And, if so, why did he want to hide that tiny chink in his armour from anyone—but more especially from her?

Did it have anything to do with those moments in the car when, so briefly, he had let her into the pain of his past, revealing for the first time the boy whose parents' 'private civil war' had made his life a personal hell?

What else had he kept hidden from her? Had she ever really known anything about this man she had once agreed to marry? And, her conscience reproved her sharply, had she ever taken the trouble to find out?

Suddenly it was as if she had slipped back in time, back to the night a year before when, with the business that had brought him north completed, Aidan had talked of returning to London.

'I don't want you to go!' she had pouted. 'I don't ever want to let you out of my sight again!'

'It will only be for a few days, Princess,' Aidan protested laughingly.

'A few days is far too long! I want you with me all the time. Every hour, every minute—every waking second! I want you there when I'm asleep too. I want to open my eyes in the morning and find you there.'

'Well, then, why don't you come with me? My place may not be the Grange, but it's more than big enough for two.'

'Move in with you?'

She could think of nothing she would like better. But then she was struck by second thoughts. Living together didn't mean commitment. What if it was only a temporary arrangement? What was to stop Aidan turning her out again if he grew tired of her? The thought made her panic.

'I don't know, Aidan. I'm not that sort of girl. I mean, it might be all very well in London, but Westbury is just a small village. People will talk.'

'Let them.'

'I can't! I live here. Marchants have been at the Grange for centuries. And besides…' she added, softly cajoling, 'I want something more permanent.'

'Marriage?' Aidan's tone was ambiguous, but she refused to let that worry her.

'That would be perfect! That way we could be together all the time, and my parents will be so pleased.'

'I doubt that's quite the way your father will feel.' Aidan's tone was wry.

'Oh, don't worry about Dad! He thinks no man is good enough for his little girl. But when I've got your ring on my finger he'll come round soon enough. He just wants me to be happy.'

'And that would do it?'

'I'd be the happiest woman alive!'

Looking back, India now saw that scene in a very different light. Aidan's voice, his expression, jarred on her in a way that, taken with what he had told her about his parents' marriage, started alarm bells ringing loudly inside her head.

But those bells hadn't sounded so clearly a year before. Had her feelings for this man blinded her to everything else, pushing aside any possible problems in the way? Or was it, as Aidan had implied, that she had been so determined to get what she wanted that she hadn't stopped to consider anyone else's point of view?

'Oh, Aidan...' she whispered softly, sadly.

As if sensing her presence, Aidan stirred slightly in his sleep, sighing faintly. India's heart twisted painfully as she saw the way the movement pulled at the open collar of his shirt, exposing the strong muscles of his shoulder, the tanned column of his throat and the shadow of dark hair on his chest.

How many times had she rested her head against the strength of that shoulder, feeling the steady beat of his heart just beneath her cheek? How many times had she pressed her lips to the warm satin of his throat and smiled in feminine triumph at his shudder of response?

His pulse would always leap in immediate reaction, his arms closing round her, the tension in his long body communicating clearly the effect she had on him, the need that flared so swiftly through both of them.

Oh, God, she could feel it now! Simply remembering, her whole body was suffused with a heat that had nothing to do with the warmth of the afternoon sun. And her heart was beating so rapidly that her blood pounded through her veins, her thoughts swimming in a burning haze of sensuality.

The aching yearning she was experiencing was no longer recalled from the past, but very much in the present. It uncoiled in the pit of her stomach, spreading rapidly

through every cell in her body, bringing her senses to
fiercely demanding life.

'India?'

For a second or two she thought the soft sound of her
name spoken in that once-loved voice was still part of her
memory, an echo from the times she had just brought to
mind.

But then the burning mist that clouded her vision cleared,
and she saw Aidan's face and realised that his eyes were
wide open and fixed on her face. Her heart jerked violently,
driving all the breath from her lungs as she met the deep
sensuality of his gaze.

That intent, lingering look was almost a caress in itself,
the slow, knowing smile that curled his mouth actually
seeming to brush her skin with warmth.

'Why don't you kiss me?' he murmured lazily, deliberately echoing her own provocative words of a week before.
'You know you want to.'

And she did, so very much. There was no point in denying the fact, even to herself, and certainly not to him.
She felt sure that her need and longing must be burning in
her eyes, etching into her skin in letters of fire. It was clear
and unambiguous, open for him to read when he looked
into her face.

But, although she knew she couldn't hide the way she
was feeling, she also knew that she was incapable of making the first move. Aidan's eyes held hers with the power
of a mesmerist's, keeping her transfixed, controlling her
with an invisible but so potent force.

'No?'

Lazy amusement lifted one dark brow, and his smile
grew wider, more deeply sensual.

'Then I'll make it easy for you, shall I?'

And, before she could register just what he had planned,
he had levered himself upright, one hand reaching out and
curling round the back of her neck. Long, powerful fingers
twisted in the blue-black strands of her hair as he drew her

face slowly and irresistibly towards his. His smile was the last thing she saw before his mouth covered hers and his head blotted out the sun.

For perhaps half a heartbeat India stiffened, unsure of how to respond. But her body had no such doubt. It was already burning with awareness—every inch of her skin, each nerve-ending awake and sensitive to everything about this man. And so it took only that one kiss to sweep away all other considerations, start up a deeply primitive, purely physical need that spiralled deep inside her, obliterating any chance of coherent thought.

She could only respond, her body pliant and unresisting, as Aidan bent her slowly backwards, never taking his lips from hers as he lowered her to the rug. The weight of his powerful frame crushed hers, pinning her to the ground so that she couldn't escape. But it was an imprisonment that she welcomed every bit as much as the heated invasion of his tongue sliding into her softened mouth and tangling with her own in a tantalising play of erotic promise.

'I've missed this.' It was a thickened mutter against her lips. 'Dear God, if you only knew how much!'

She did know, India told herself. How could she not know when her own response was as wild and fierce as a forest fire, taking her into a white-hot world where nothing existed but Aidan and herself? Where nothing mattered but his kisses, the burning touch of those strong, knowing hands as they roved over her body.

That touch was becoming more urgent now, tugging her T-shirt loose from the waistband of her jeans and pushing it roughly upwards.

'Thank God for summer,' Aidan muttered, discarding the flimsy garment to discover that, because of the heat, she wore no bra underneath. 'You are *so* lovely!'

His second comment was murmured against the soft flesh of her exposed breasts, making India cry aloud in response to the warm caress of his breath on her skin, the heated touch of his mouth. She couldn't tell whether the pounding she could hear was the sound of the waterfall thundering over the rocks behind her or the frantic racing of her own pulse sending the blood throbbing through her veins.

She could no longer lie still and submissive. The need to touch him back was uncontrollable. She wanted to feel the strong, honed muscles, run her fingers down the taut lines of his body without the restriction of clothing. Thank God for summer, indeed, she thought devoutly as Aidan's shirt followed her own, tossed aside with careless indifference to where it fell.

'I want…'

It was a frantic plea, the near desperation of her tone matched by the impatient fumbling of her fingers as they struggled with the fastening of his belt.

'So do I, honey, believe me…' was the half-laughing, half-choked response as he came to her aid, his hands only marginally more confident.

Between them they disposed of the restricting buckle and the zip on his jeans, allowing her access to more intimate areas of his body.

She had forgotten how good he felt. Forgotten how warm and smooth his skin was. Forgotten too the contrast between its softness and the power of the muscles beneath, like steel sheathed in velvet, so that touching him was pure delight. Her fingers stroked, massaged, occasionally clenching tight.

'Do you know what that does to me? Can you even begin to guess…?'

If Aidan's voice had been husky before, now it was positively raw, tight with a need that sent a thrill of purely feminine triumph searing through her at the thought that she was the one who had brought him to this pitch.

'I don't need to guess,' she murmured provocatively, her smiling lips very close to his ear. 'I *know*. I have undeniable proof.'

And with a light-hearted chuckle she trailed her fingertips down his chest, sliding them between their two bodies and closing over the physical evidence of his desire for her. Her smile grew wider as his powerful body bucked beneath her soft touch, his breathing hissing in through his teeth in reaction.

'All right, you asked for it!' he declared thickly, and proceeded to subject her to an unremittingly sensual assault, using every trick he knew, every pleasure-giving touch she remembered—and some that were completely new—to bring her totally under his erotic control.

India found that she was writhing under the delicious torment of his hands, losing all control when his warmly wicked mouth closed over first one and then the other of her breasts. His lips tugged softly on each aroused nipple in a way that had her moaning her delight.

It seemed as if a fierce electric current had seared its way from each sensitised tip straight to the juncture of her thighs, centring in the very core of her femininity. Slowly the pressure of need built until it was so intense it was very close to pain. Her body was screaming with hunger and excitement, her pulse a pounding thunder that drowned out the roar of the waterfall at her back.

She couldn't keep still, but crushed herself against Aidan's hard strength, twisting underneath him, arching in silent demand for the final, ultimate union of their bodies. And when at last his hot, muscular legs slid between hers, spreading them wide, she found she had caught her lower lip in her teeth, digging in hard against the cry of yearning that almost escaped her.

Aidan's breathing was fractured, his heartbeat as frantic and uneven as her own. The dark eyes that stared down into hers were all black, no trace of brown even at the outer rim. They were glazed with an incandescent passion that, even as she welcomed it, also made her heart skip a beat in fearful anticipation of its wild intensity.

'I've been without this for so long, darling,' Aidan muttered as he fitted himself up against her, so close and yet not close enough. 'Too long—too damn long!'

The final words came on a gasping cry of fulfilment as he finally lost control and drove into her welcoming body. His hands came under her hips to gather her closer as they gave themselves up to the savage, primitive rhythm of the senses.

India felt as if her veins had been flooded with molten gold. She couldn't see, couldn't hear, only knew she was lost in a boiling whirlwind of sensation. It had caught her up and swung her out of reality. She was being carried higher and higher until at last, with a final cry that was half a sigh and half a sob of pure ecstasy, it climaxed in a heart-stopping moment when stars were actually exploding in the sky around her.

A couple of heartbeats later, Aidan too reached his release, his head going back, his back arching, her name a raw sound on his lips. Then he collapsed against her with a sigh of completion that seemed to come from the depths of his soul.

It was a long, long time before either of them could breathe naturally again. India's racing heart slowed so gradually that it was only when Aidan moved, rolling from her to lie on the grass, one arm over his eyes, that she realised she was once more hearing the waterfall, and not her own pulse inside her head.

What had she done? *What had she done?* The question swung round and round inside her head, providing no answer no matter how many times she faced it.

She didn't know if she was glad or sorry about what had happened. She only knew that it had been inevitable since the day Aidan had come back into her life—inevitable and unstoppable as an avalanche, and nothing she could have done would have changed a thing.

At long last Aidan sighed and sat up slowly, reaching for his clothes. He didn't even look in her direction, but passed her T-shirt and shorts to her without a word, not speaking until they were both fully dressed.

'We should make a move soon.'

'Do we have to?'

India found that she didn't want this time to end. The little clearing seemed like a magical place, isolated from a reality she didn't want to face. For that reason she didn't dare to look directly at Aidan, not wanting to see his expression, fearful of what his eyes might reveal to her of his thoughts.

So she stared fixedly at the ground, concentrating her attention on the wanderings of an ant as if her life depended on being able to map out its route again later.

'You know we do, Princess. Your mother will begin to wonder where we are.'

'No, she won't. She'll know I'm with you and so, in Mum's opinion, perfectly safe.'

Instead of which she was, emotionally at least, in far greater danger than ever in her life before.

In the past she had believed herself in love with Aidan—but now, to her cost, she knew that what she had experienced then had been only the weak beginnings of any such feeling. She had known just the first tiny shoots of what had since grown into a strong, deeply rooted plant.

The moments in Aidan's arms, the passion they had shared here in this sunlit glade, had simply confirmed what she had known for some time but had been afraid to acknowledge. She loved and needed Aidan with all the strength and power of which her heart was capable.

When she was with him, she flowered. Without him, she very much feared that she would shrivel and die. It had been terrible enough to lose him the first time; she had no idea how she would cope if he ever left her again.

'Your mother obviously doesn't share your father's low opinion of me.'

'She doesn't agree with his concern with family name and status, true,' India agreed. 'She was pushed into marrying Dad by her parents. It was almost an arranged marriage between two of the county's most important families.'

'But she made it work. She cares for him now.' A new

note had crept into Aidan's voice, one she had never heard before.

'Oh, yes.' A sudden smile lit up India's face. 'She grew to love him—in spite of himself, she always says. He's not an easy man to get close to, you see. He doesn't have the emotional vocabulary to talk about his feelings.'

He was like Aidan in that, she reflected, recalling how reluctant he had been to reveal any personal details to her.

'Few men have,' Aidan put in gruffly. 'But what will happen now?'

'Now?'

Surprise brought India's head round in a rush. But whatever emotion lurked in those brown depths was unreadable, impossible to interpret.

'When she finds out about the gambling—the debts.'

'I think she'll cope.'

But even as she spoke India's heart clenched painfully. For a brief space of time she had actually managed to forget about the events of the past week, the real reason why Aidan was here. It was as if the blazing passion she had just experienced had burned from her mind all thought of the hold he had over her and her family.

'She loves him for what he is.' Inner distress sharpened her tone. 'I don't think she's ever had any illusions about him.'

'And what about you?'

'If you really love someone, you accept them as they are.' It was only as she said the words aloud that she realised how true they were. 'Warts and all, as Oliver Cromwell put it.'

And she could accept Aidan in that way too, could even forgive him for the way he had treated her.

With a background like his, it was only natural that the prospect of marriage was not one that would appeal to him. If only she had known that earlier, then she wouldn't have pushed for marriage so soon. She would have given him time to get to know her better, to love…

Love. That was the vital word, the one that touched everything. If Aidan only loved her she could face anything, forgive anything. In fact, hadn't she already done so without being asked, simply because she loved him?

But what did he feel for her?

'And anyway, you're wrong about Dad's opinion of you. By the day of our wedding he'd come round to our marriage. In fact, in the end he was quite happy—'

'I'll bet he was.'

Aidan was fastening his shoe, the force with which he pulled on the laces revealing the strength of the cynicism he had injected into his words. Hearing it, India frowned her confusion.

'And just what does that mean?'

'Oh, come on, Princess!' Aidan mocked, his face set into inimical lines, his eyes merciless. 'You can't have been unaware of the fact that your father knew exactly on what side his bread was buttered, and was determined to take advantage of it. He was prepared to ignore my lack of suitable ancestry when he realised just how much hard cash I would put into the family coffers.'

'No...'

Words failed her completely, the need to refute Aidan's hateful accusation fading before a devastating rush of memory.

From being totally opposed to the idea of her marrying at all, her father had suddenly and inexplicably come round to the situation. In fact, he had seemed all for it, and had started to spend money like water on flowers, champagne, the reception. Money she now knew he had never actually possessed.

'How much did you lend him?' she croaked, wincing as Aidan flung at her an amount that sounded like a telephone number in a voice that was thick with contempt.

'So much. And you paid it!'

'It seemed worth it at the time.'

It was no wonder he had believed her capable of meaning

that mercenary bet she had made with Jane. No wonder he had thought she was so much her father's daughter that she had tried to take him for every penny she could get. So much so that he had accepted her father's demands for a financial gift without quibbling, believing the impetus came from her.

'So it was true about the pre-nuptial agreement.'

Her voice was just a thin thread of sound, and it was a statement, not a question, because she already knew the answer. Nervously she picked daisies from the grass, gathering them into a small bunch in her hands.

'Whatever else you may think of me, Princess,' Aidan flung at her, 'I've never lied to you.'

And that, she knew, was nothing but the truth. If she hadn't already believed it, the raw violence of his tone would have convinced her at once.

'Oh, God, Aidan—I'm so very sorry!'

For a long, silent moment, Aidan simply stared into her face, his eyes strangely unfocused. But then suddenly he laughed with shocking harshness.

'Do you know, Princess, for a second there I almost believed you? You were very convincing.'

'Because I mean it!'

She reached out to grasp his hand, only to have him move it out of reach in a swift, careless movement.

'I didn't know what my father was doing; I had no idea! But now that I do know it starts to explain things. I think I see why you behaved as you did.'

'Do you?'

She couldn't read the shadowed undertones in his question, couldn't begin to understand what had put them there, and so could only continue as if he hadn't spoken.

'I can only wonder why you ever turned up at the church at all.'

'Believe me, there are times when I ask myself that question too. Perhaps I just wanted one last look at your lovely face—and the body that had given me so much pleasure.'

The pain that throwaway comment brought was agonising, forcing India to her feet, unable to sit close to him any longer. Aidan proceeded to pack away the picnic food and plates, his actions seeming to underline the casual cruelty of his remark.

'You can't expect me to accept that! If you'd wanted me so much, you could have gone through with the wedding anyway. Then you could have…have…'

One hand clenched on the daisies she still held, crushing them savagely as her voice died in her throat, seeming to shrivel up in the blazing force of the look he turned on her pale face.

'Had you whenever I wanted? Is that what you were trying to say, my lovely India? The thought did cross my mind, but that would have been taking the easy way out.'

'The *easy*…'

India shook her head helplessly. None of this fitted with what he had said earlier. Then he had declared that he had arrived at the church still planning to marry her, that making her his wife would have been the cruellest thing he could have done.

'So you didn't want—us.' Hastily she substituted the less inflammatory word for the provocative 'me' she had originally meant to use. 'Not at all. You just wanted your revenge, just as you do now. They say revenge is a dish best eaten cold—but I would never have thought it was worth waiting for so long.'

Belatedly she became aware of the way that her nerveless fingers were shredding the flowers in her hands, pulling off the delicate petals in a dark parody of the old superstition, 'He loves me, he loves me not'. Hastily she stilled them, fearful of what they revealed.

'You have a dangerous tendency to exaggerate,' Aidan put in with hateful reasonableness. 'I could hardly have predicted that your father would have a stroke just before the repayment of his loan was due.'

'I don't suppose you could, but it must have been an unexpected bonus for you,' India told him bitterly.

'Let's just say it made things a lot easier.'

'I'll just bet it did! It meant that with my father out of the way you had just the lever you needed to move into the Grange and take over!'

Her heart jolted nervously as Aidan's hand tightened on the plate he had just picked up, the force of his feelings making his knuckles show white.

'Have you ever considered that your father might have been better off with me than some I could think of?' he snarled, his anger flaring suddenly. 'There are those who wouldn't have given him those six months interest free, who would have—'

'Interest free!' India cut in sharply. 'You never said anything about that before.'

From the look that crossed Aidan's face, the flicker of a new emotion deep in his eyes, she knew that he had never meant to let that particular fact slip out. But now he had, and those two simple words altered the balance of the situation once again.

'Well, one thing's for sure. The money from this prenuptial agreement—every penny of it's yours!'

'To pay off your father's debts?' Aidan's fury had subsided as suddenly as it had come, now his words were icily controlled. 'You must love him very much.'

'No, *not* to pay off anything! I can't take that money, Aidan; it wouldn't be right. I never asked my father to negotiate anything with you, and I won't profit from his actions. You must take it all back.'

'India, there's no need!' Aidan cut in harshly. 'I signed that money over to you, and, financially, I never missed it. It was always meant to be yours and I want you to have it.'

'Well, I don't want it! And particularly not when I know how it was acquired.'

'Well, you can do what you like with it, but I won't

touch any of it. If you try to give it to me, I'll burn the cheque and send you back the ashes.'

The declaration was flat, emotionless, but nevertheless imbued with a deadly force that left India in no doubt at all that he meant every word he said.

'So what now?'

'Now?'

Aidan had finished packing away the picnic things, and now he got to his feet, picking up the rug and folding it neatly. Without its colourful covering, the glade suddenly seemed empty and unappealing, matching the desolate feeling in India's heart.

Only moments before she had told herself that things could be forgiven and forgotten if only Aidan would tell her that he loved her. Now she knew she had only been fooling herself. He was never going to say any such thing. If anything, they seemed further apart now than at any time, even the moment when he had turned and walked away from her at their wedding.

'I think that's really up to you.'

'To me?'

Aidan nodded slowly, his expression tightly controlled as he dropped the folded rug on top of the picnic basket. The impregnable armour was once more securely back in place, not a single chink showing in its gleaming, protective surface.

'I think what happened here...'

Deliberately he let his gaze slide to the ground at their feet, lingering on the spots where the weight of their bodies had crushed the soft grass. But already the flattened stalks were beginning to recover, to spring back into place. In a few more minutes it would look as if they had never been there at all.

'Proves that there's still something very strong between us—something I'd like more of.'

'You'd want a relationship with an emotional vampire?' India's voice slid up and down in the most disturbing way.

'I thought that was the role you had assigned to me,' Aidan murmured softly, with a slanted glance at her face that brought a wash of hot colour into her cheeks.

Not waiting for any reply, or well aware of the fact that she was incapable of finding one, he went on smoothly, 'I'm prepared to accept that you knew nothing of the money your father borrowed from me before we were married. And if, as you claim, the idea of the bet with your friend was nothing more than a joke—'

'It *was*!' India put in urgently. 'Believe me, it was!'

It was only when Aidan paused, a frown drawing his dark brows together, that she wondered if she had moved too quickly. She couldn't quite put her finger on precisely why, but she was left with a suspicion that there should have been more, that something vital had been left unsaid— but she had no idea what.

But at last Aidan nodded slowly, some of the coldness going out of his expression, though there was still no trace of anything even remotely resembling any warmth.

'Then, if you want, we could carry on from here and see where it takes us.'

The frightening thing was how easy it was to consider his emotionless proposition. Already she was halfway towards accepting it, in her own mind at least.

She loved Aidan. She loved him enough to take the little he was prepared to offer and, if not be content with it, then at least find some degree of happiness in the time they spent together.

'I… There's one thing I need to know first.'

'And that is?'

'My father—the money he owes you and all the rest of it. Does the way you'll treat him depend on…?'

'On the way you behave?' Aidan finished for her when she floundered over the words. 'On whether you please me in bed?'

Slowly he shook his head, heavy lids hooding his eyes, hiding his thoughts from her.

'This is just between you and I, Princess. No one else has any part in it.'

Just between you and I. It had an unexpectedly reassuring sound.

Perhaps on those terms they *could* try again. Perhaps just the two of them, with no interference from outside forces like her father, could rediscover the things that had brought them together in the first place. And perhaps, while the passion that blazed between them wasn't enough to build a future on, it might at least hold them together long enough to allow something else, something stronger and more lasting, to grow in its place.

'But there's one thing I want you to be clear on. I'm not talking about marriage. There's nothing like that in prospect. I don't put my neck in the same noose a second time.'

The words were as hard and unyielding as his expression. Simply listening to him felt like banging her head against a very hard, very rigid brick wall. It would do no good to plead or protest; he simply wouldn't hear her.

'I'm not asking for marriage,' India managed, exerting every ounce of self-control she possessed in order to keep her voice even. At least that undeniable passion showed one thing—it meant that he felt *something*, that he wasn't completely indifferent to her. 'Like you, I'm happy with what there is. I don't want anything more.'

But even as she spoke she was hearing again inside her head the way that Aidan had spoken of his parents, of the mutual desire that had bound them together until their inability to love had torn them apart.

'You don't have to have love for it.' His harsh tones seemed to beat against her skull, making her want to put her head in her hands for fear it might actually crack under the strain. 'It isn't an essential ingredient for brilliant sex.'

So could she accept the sex without any hope of love?

Aidan had denied that he hated her. He had admitted that he wanted her, had demonstrated that only too clearly in this glade just a short time before, so she could have no doubt that he meant it. But was it enough?

Could she really be content with so little? Could she take what he offered and never ask for more?

'I'm happy with what there is,' she had said, knowing the words to be a lie. She could never be truly happy when she was starving and Aidan was only prepared to toss her a few inadequate crumbs. But if she let him see the way she really felt he would turn and walk away from her, reject her completely. And if he did that her life would be totally destroyed. There was no way she could ever fill the emptiness he would leave behind.

So there was no decision to make in the end. Deep down, she knew she had no option but to go along with Aidan's conditions. It was that or nothing at all.

CHAPTER ELEVEN

'AIDAN, I have something for you.'

India's voice was as unsteady as her hands, which were clenched tightly around the box she was holding in an effort to hide the way they shook.

'For me?'

If she had been nervous before, then the feeling was made even worse as Aidan's dark head lifted from the papers spread out over the table before him. His narrow-eyed scrutiny made her feel supremely conscious of her body in the sleeveless red linen dress she wore, its bodice smoothly close-fitting while the skirt flared out softly from her hips.

She had carefully chosen this moment when both her mother and brother were at the hospital to approach him, but now she was no longer so sure of the wisdom of her decision. Ever since the day of the picnic, being alone with Aidan at the Grange had felt like walking a very shaky tightrope above a furiously racing river.

The wild undercurrents of sensual awareness seemed to whirl and coil around her until her head swam. Simply being in the same room as him made her feel as if she had stuffed her fingers into a live electric socket and let a powerful current crackle through her.

'And what have I done to deserve a present?'

'Well, it's more something I want to give you *back*.'

India struggled to ignore the dark note of irony that threaded through his voice.

'I should have done it ages ago. I just never felt that the time was right before now.'

With an awkward movement she put the package down

on the library table, taking a hasty step backwards immediately.

Aidan stared down at it, a frown drawing his brows together as he studied the brown-paper-wrapped parcel. His long body stiffened sharply as he took in the original address label with his own name on it, the stamps postmarked with a date a year before. That label had been ruthlessly scored through, and the words RETURN TO SENDER scrawled beside it.

'But this is…'

With those brilliant, piercing eyes on her face, India gave a jerky little nod.

'I sent it to you when you walked out on me.'

And he had posted it straight back to her. Or, rather, his secretary had done so on his instructions. India knew that because she had originally received it carefully rewrapped and with a polite covering note that belied the hostility of the words on the original paper.

'I didn't want anything from you,' Aidan growled, and India gave a small, sharp laugh, one that sounded painfully lacking in any trace of humour.

'That was exactly how I felt too. That's why I sent you this. These things aren't *for* you, but from you.'

'What?'

That frown deepening, Aidan reached for the parcel and ripped off the paper. His movements rough, he shook the box open so that its contents spilled out onto the table in tumbled disarray.

In a moment of stunned silence he studied the bundle of varied items, a closed, unreadable expression on his face.

'Everything.' It was a low, harsh-toned mutter, as if only meant for himself. 'Every damned thing I ever gave you.'

'Except the flowers, of course,' India put in jerkily.

But Aidan wasn't listening. Long fingers drifted over the pile of gifts, then suddenly closed on one particular item with a snatching movement that made her nerves twist in reaction. When he flicked open the ring box one-handed, she couldn't meet his eyes.

'I believe it is acceptable for the jilted fiancée to keep the ring.' Each word seemed formed in ice.

'Not to me, it isn't!' India declared vehemently. 'And particularly not now! My father used our engagement as an opportunity to take from you in a way that was wrong. It was greedy and selfish, and I don't want our family to take anything more from you. You bought me these things when I was going to marry you. Now that there is nothing between us...'

'Nothing?'

'Nothing!'

She repeated the word deliberately, using the forceful emphasis to drive away the disturbing thoughts that drawling question brought to mind. She knew only too well what was in Aidan's thoughts.

Determinedly she kept her eyes fixed on the table, knowing that to see his face, the way that she knew one eyebrow would have lifted in cynical questioning, would destroy her. It wasn't cowardice that had stopped her from giving him any sort of answer to his emotionless proposal, but the simple fact that she couldn't think of one.

For days now she had veered back and forth between acceptance and vehement rejection, struggling with the question night after night in the darkness of her room. She couldn't accept so little, she had told herself, but had been unable to come up with any answer to the problem of how she would cope with the nothing that was inevitably the only possible alternative.

To his credit, Aidan hadn't tried to rush her, but neither had he shown any sign of being prepared to consider any possible alternative. His desire for her was clear. It showed in the darkness of his eyes when he looked at her; she could hear it in the husky note in his voice in almost every word he addressed to her.

She could be in no doubt as to what he wanted, just as

there was no way she could delude herself that he would
stay around for long if he didn't get exactly what he had
set his heart on. Or, rather, not his *heart,* brutal reality
forced her to amend on a bitter stab of pain.

'These won't go any way towards repaying even part of
the money we owe you, but at least it will be something.
It will salve my conscience just a little.'

'I meant you to keep them when I bought them for you,'
Aidan stated flatly.

'But you must see that I can't do that now! There's some
expensive jewellery here.'

'Quite frankly, the money is irrelevant to me.'

'But it isn't just a question of money! Can't you see that
I couldn't live with myself if I didn't do something, however small? I want you to...'

Her voice failed her, drying to a painful squeak as Aidan
suddenly dropped the ring box and, pushing aside an elegant watch, pounced on a new and very different item.

Something savage clawed at India's soul, leaving it raw
and bleeding as she recognised the small black figure that
seemed so incongruous amongst the glitter of gold chains,
the blue leather jewellery boxes.

'The funfair,' Aidan declared harshly. 'The hoopla stall.'

India could only nod silently, unable to avoid his eyes
any longer. What she saw there made her want to turn and
run, put as much distance between herself and Aidan as
was physically possible. But she had started this. She had
to finish it too, no matter how painful it might be.

'You fell in love with it as soon as you saw it.'

'And you were determined to win it for me.'

Her voice was just a croak. She could still recall as if it
were yesterday just how she had felt when she had seen
the little black pottery cat with the bright green glass eyes.
It had been such a special day, only the second date they
had shared, and certainly one of the happiest she and Aidan
had ever had together.

The fair had been an unusually simple pleasure for the

two of them. As a child, India had always loved such things, and when she had learned that it was to be set up on the village green she hadn't been able to hide her excitement. She had pestered Aidan about it until, obviously faintly bemused by her enthusiasm, he had agreed to take her.

There couldn't have been a greater contrast between the shabby, unsophisticated funfair and the expensive, exclusive nightclub to which he had taken her the previous evening. India had taken a child-like delight in the battered dodgem cars and the merry-go-round with its gaudily painted dancing horses. She had laughed at the ill-made spectres on the ghost train, and even inhaled appreciatively, drawing in the heavy aroma of hot dogs and candyfloss on the air.

'You must have spent a fortune on that stall.' Her voice was as raw as her feelings, the sentence breaking revealingly in the middle.

'It was so small. The rings just seemed to skim straight over it.'

This time, when their eyes met, India felt as though her mind was spinning, throwing her off balance, so that she actually swayed on her feet. When had that glow appeared in the depths of his eyes, warming and softening them? She could hardly believe that the same man stood before her.

This man was so very different, was such a poignant reminder of the Aidan of a year ago, the man she had fallen in love with, that it went straight to her unprotected heart like a burning arrow.

'But you wanted it, and so I wanted it for you.'

His smile was lop-sided, gently reminiscent in a way that twisted the arrow-head painfully.

'I—I thought it would bring me luck.'

She couldn't bring herself to admit that she had convinced herself superstitiously that if only Aidan could win the little cat for her, then it meant that *she* would win his love.

As a result, it had ceased to be a cute but cheap ornament and had become a symbol of all her hopes and dreams, the longing that had kept her wide awake at night.

'And I thought it looked rather like you, with its jet-black colouring and those vivid emerald eyes. I would have done anything to get it for you.' Aidan shook his head as if in disbelief at his memories. 'At that time, I couldn't think straight, didn't know who I was half of the time. I would have done anything for you.'

'To get me into your bed,' India corrected sharply.

He didn't deny it. 'I wanted you so much that I ached all over. I thought I was actually ill.'

His laugh was raw, strangely shaken.

'That was probably why my aim was so badly off. Usually I'm much more skilful than that.'

He hadn't had to wait long, India recalled, closing her eyes briefly against the twist of pain the memory brought. It had been that same night that they had become lovers.

With the little cat safely in her hands at last, and high on the atmosphere and the sheer physical magnetism of the man at her side, she had been more intoxicated with happiness than she had ever been as the result of any sort of alcohol.

'What happened to us, India?'

Her eyes snapped open in shock, green gaze meeting deep brown, seeing a flame burning in that darkness that sent a frisson of intense awareness shivering down her spine.

'We were completely different people then.' Her words sounded rough round the edges.

'Not so very different,' Aidan returned, low-voiced. 'You can still make me feel the same way about you—in one way, at least. I still ache to possess you every bit as much as I did that night—more.'

'I'm no man's possession!'

'Oh, no, Princess. No one could ever tie you down in

that way. But you were all that I wanted and more. A fantasy come true.'

If he looked as deeply into her face as she had done into his, then he must know that she felt the same. He would read it in her eyes, detect it in the heightened rate of her pulse that made her breathing rapid and uneven. If she let him see that, he would know once and for all just how she felt—and she would be lost.

Hastily she reached for another item from the bundle on the table, this one wrapped in decorative paper.

'This is for you as well,' she said sharply. 'Well, go on—open it!'

She couldn't bear to watch as he tore off the wrapping; she only knew when he had opened the parcel by the sudden silence, the stillness of the man beside her.

'The watercolour,' Aidan said at last, the words strangely uneven. 'You bought it.'

'It was supposed to be a wedding present.' She couldn't disguise her bitterness.

They had seen the painting in the window of an antiques shop just before the wedding, and Aidan had fallen in love with it. He would have bought it then and there, but the shop had been closed, the owner on holiday. India had sneaked back there as soon as it had reopened, while Aidan was in London. She had bought the picture and hidden it away, meaning to give it to him on their wedding night, pretending all the time that someone else had beaten her to it.

'But you couldn't afford it.'

'I managed,' India declared, her voice brittle. It had taken every penny of her savings, but she wasn't prepared to admit that. 'And now you can take it as part payment of our debt to you. If you're lucky you might even find its value's increased over the year.'

'I can't...'

'Oh, yes, you can. You must.'

She had to do something to disguise her inner turmoil,

to distract herself from the way her wanton body was already yearning towards his as if she were a fine steel needle drawn by some uncontrollable magnetism. Taking the only opportunity available to her, she moved impulsively, coming closer to the table and looking down at the papers on it, touching them lightly with her fingertips.

A moment later she found her interest caught and held, her attention fully focused on what she now realised were plans of the Grange. The improvements Aidan had already set in motion were clearly marked—as were, she now realised, other more ambitious projects.

'A swimming pool, Aidan?' She tried to make it sound light-hearted, but only succeeded in sounding arch and brittle. 'Isn't that going rather over the top?'

'Not at all.'

He was well aware of her deliberate diversionary tactics; the stiffness of his response told her that without the need for any further evidence.

'There's plenty of space for one at the back, where it will be completely private, and I thought it would be good for your father when he comes home. He'll need to convalesce, and I'm sure they'll advise him that light exercise... Why are you looking at me like that?'

'I'm finding it hard to believe. Would you do that for him?'

'Not for him, India,' he correctly sternly. 'For your mother. I've come to admire her greatly over the past couple of weeks. She's devoted herself selflessly to your father without any complaints or self-pity, even when she's obviously so exhausted she can barely stand upright. For the first time in my life, I'm beginning to believe that such a thing as real love can actually exist.'

It took all India's control not to flinch outwardly as well as deep inside, not to reveal the pain he had inflicted by that last, cool-voiced statement. If he had never really believed in love, then their past relationship and his proposal of marriage had been founded on something else entirely.

And she could be in no doubt as to just what baser motives had been behind it.

'I wanted you, you wanted me,' he had declared once with callous bluntness. 'I would have done anything.' *Anything*—even offer to marry her.

But she was forgetting the dreadful story he had told her about his parents.

'I suppose you didn't exactly get much chance to learn about love from your parents. How old were you when they died?'

'Nearly fifteen.' It was tossed at her with no emotion behind it, his eyes hooded and secretive.

'A difficult age.' Her heart ached for the lost and lonely adolescent he must have been. 'What did you do then?'

'For a time I went completely wild. I played truant, ran away from every foster home they put me in. I drank too much, hung around with some street gangs, got in trouble with the law. Oh, yes...'

He had caught her expression, responding with a grim, cold smile that made her blood turn to ice.

'Back then, I earned every word of the reputation I gained. I thought the world owed me something, and I was determined to get it any way I could. But I soon realised that I was losing more than ever, carrying on the way I was.'

Roughly, Aidan pushed both hands through the glossy darkness of his hair, the gesture far more expressive of his inner feelings than his carefully controlled expression and blanked-out eyes.

'I saw that I was letting the legacy of my parents' mess leach into my life and screw it up just as much as it had destroyed theirs. So I pulled myself up sharp, vowed I'd make something of my future.'

'You've certainly done that. You have everything...'

'Everything?' Aidan queried sardonically, turning a look of black cynicism on her.

'Well, you've made a fortune. You'd never have to work

again if you didn't want to. And now you've got yourself the perfect country house which you're restoring to look exactly as you want it.'

'You're easily satisfied if you think that's everything.'

Something dangerous lurked underneath the words, dark and ominous like the jagged rocks at the bottom of apparently calm waters, just waiting to rip the heart out of a passing boat.

'Though, I have to admit, I once believed something very much the same myself. If love didn't exist, then I'd replace it with something much more tangible, something I could actually *see*, so I'd know it was real, not just a figment of people's romantic fantasies. I set myself to making a fortune, and then, when I'd done that, making another. And, yes, I admit I earned my reputation in that field as well. I know what they call me.'

The Lone Wolfe. The words echoed inside India's head. She had used them herself so often in connection with Aidan—but now she suddenly found herself putting the emphasis on the 'Lone', rather than the 'Wolfe'.

'You could easily change that.' It took all her strength to say it.

'Marry, you mean? I don't think so. With my parents' example behind me, I promised myself that I would only ever marry someone I knew I loved, and who loved me in return. Someone with whom I could have a real future, a deep relationship like your mother has with your father. I wouldn't settle for anything less. I made that mistake the first time, and I've rued it ever since.'

It was perfectly cool, completely matter-of-fact. There had been no emotion in that 'the first time', but all the same it had felt to India as if the words were cruel, vicious claws ripping at her heart. She need look no further for the real explanation for the way he had walked out on her on their wedding day.

He had never really loved her. He had 'thought he could

go through with it'. But at the last moment the spectre of his parents' marriage had raised its ugly head and made him realise just what a mistake he had been about to make.

CHAPTER TWELVE

'SO WE'RE agreed I'm not marriage material.' Aidan's cold flippancy was devastating. 'But what about you? Surely you will marry. You'll want children.'

India's blood chilled at the recollection of the way the same topic had come up between them once before. She'd asked him if he wanted a family and he had responded with a biting harshness that had stunned and shocked her. The memory put a shake in her voice as she answered.

'I'd love kids. Two at least.'

The image in her mind of a boy and a girl, sharing Aidan's dark hair, his deep brown eyes, was so sharp with longing that she felt sure it must communicate itself to him by some form of instinctive telepathy. But his next comment made it only too plain that his thoughts were running on very different lines.

'With Jim?'

'No—not Jim.'

She couldn't give him anything less than complete honesty. A lie, or even a half-truth, would stick in her throat.

'Like you, I always believed in that real, special love.'

He had been studying the plans on the table, but now his head came up slowly.

'And Jim isn't the one? I admit it doesn't surprise me. Quite frankly, I've always felt he was a little—under-enthusiastic.'

The throwaway casualness of the comment hurt more than any outright attack. If he hated her, as she had once accused him of doing, or thought very badly of her, then at least she would have something to fight. Aidan's indifference seemed to drain all the emotional strength from her, leaving her limp and flat as a deflated balloon.

'I think I only turned to him for comfort. I was lonely.'

'I'm sorry.' Aidan said unexpectedly. 'We really screwed each other up, didn't we, Princess?'

'But perhaps we learned a lot in the process.'

'Like what, precisely?'

'Well, that we really didn't—communicate—properly.'

Couldn't he see what she was trying to say? Couldn't he read the need, the longing in her eyes? Hadn't he been listening to what she had said?

'You're right, we didn't.' It was a flat declaration of fact. 'I mean, this...'

Leaning forward, he pressed a soft, heartbreakingly brief kiss on her cheek, his warm breath stirring her hair gently.

'And this...'

Another kiss, brushed lightly across her mouth, made her gasp faintly, her lips opening instinctively in response to the hot ache that woke deep within her, uncoiling swiftly to send a flood of molten heat through her veins.

'Are forms of communication, ways of letting another person know the way we feel about them. But they're strictly limited, and where you and I are concerned they're just not accurate.'

'Aren't they?'

The words slipped past her guard because she was adrift on a sea of yearning, incapable of holding them back.

'No.' It was low, the single syllable drawn out almost to a sigh. 'They're very far from the whole truth.'

But then he drew back very slightly, looking deep into her eyes, and suddenly became very still.

India found her gaze held by a force that seemed to want to draw out her soul from her body. The only small part of her that could move was her tongue, wetting her painfully dry lips with a nervous, flickering movement.

Just for a second Aidan's dark gaze dropped, focused on her mouth. But then, as at last she found herself able to draw a deep, uneven breath, he looked up again. This time, as their eyes clashed once more, he made a sound in his throat that was neither an expression of exasperation nor one of capitulation, but a disturbing mixture of the two.

'Oh, what the hell!' he muttered thickly. 'It will do for now. Come here…'

He reached for her roughly, almost clumsily, pulling her close, crushing her against his chest as his mouth came down hard on hers.

India could do nothing but respond on a purely instinctive level. Beyond thought, beyond caring exactly how he meant what he had said or even why he had said it, she only knew that this was what she wanted most in all the world.

'Damn it to hell!' Aidan muttered roughly.

And then he had swung her off her feet, holding her in strong, imprisoning arms as he carried her up the stairs and along the landing. Pausing only long enough to kick his bedroom door open, he crossed the blue carpet with swift, urgent strides, depositing her on the bed with more urgency than gentleness.

'I can't think of anything else,' he declared before his mouth took hers, his lips fiercely demanding.

His hands were busy with the buttons on her dress, dispensing with them swiftly and efficiently, then pushing the scarlet material from her shoulder and down her arms, exposing the white curves of her breasts above a lacy froth of a bra.

'Then don't think.' It was all India could manage, the hunger that gripped her running through her body like wildfire. 'Don't think at all—just love me.'

'You've got it, lady,' he assured her thickly.

Within seconds, it seemed, their clothes were discarded and their naked limbs tangled together, mouths burning against each other, tasting, nibbling, biting. Aidan's hands were hot on her skin, awakening pleasure in the same seconds that they added to the frustration of her need.

Becoming aware of the fact that he was holding back, restraining himself for her, she gave a little moan of impatience.

She didn't need consideration, didn't want restraint. She wanted Aidan inside her now.

'Now!' Dimly she heard a voice that she barely recognised as her own urging him on, her body opening to him, fingers clenching in the muscles of his strong shoulder. 'Now, Aidan, take me now.'

Then they were one, locked together, moving together. Once more that primitive rhythm took them over, taking them closer, closer—and finally right over the edge, into the blazing volcano of burning, pulsing fulfilment.

Afterwards she curled up beside him, her head on his shoulder, hearing the racing of his heart gradually slow. In the silence her thoughts went back to the conversation they had had and when at last she had the strength to talk she stirred slightly, lifting her head to look into his face.

'Aidan...' she began hesitantly. 'What you're prepared to do for my father—I want you to know that I'm so grateful. I don't know how we'll ever be able to repay you.'

'Repay?'

To her horror, his voice had sharpened harshly, and there was a new and disturbing tension in the long body lying beside her. Every trace of the lazily contented mood had gone, and his tone was clipped and curt when he spoke again.

'*Grateful!* Repayment!' he repeated, lacing each word with a deadly violence that was somehow all the more frightening because his voice hadn't been raised above a ruthlessly controlled, unnatural softness. 'Was that all this was, India? Just payment in kind?'

'Of course not! I wasn't being *kind*!'

'Then what *were* you being?'

'I...'

But even as she hunted for an answer, knowing there was no way she could find one that would satisfy him, her thoughts were suddenly dragged on to other, more practical concerns. The sound of a car coming up the drive broke into their secluded little world, and had her leaping from the bed.

'It's my mother! She's back early. If she finds me like this…!'

'She knows you're an adult.' Aidan dismissed her concern with a shrug. 'And we are supposed to be together…'

'But not like this!'

How could she let her mother walk in on a scenario that she couldn't begin to explain properly, even to herself? She had told herself that she couldn't accept Aidan's loveless passion, and yet all he had to do was touch her and she had fallen straight into his arms—into his bed.

The only way that she could justify her weakness would be to say that she had done it out of love. She knew now that her love for Aidan would always make her vulnerable where he was concerned. But she couldn't tell her mother that—certainly not until she had tried to tell Aidan himself.

'Here…'

Rolling off the bed, Aidan tossed her clothes towards her in a gesture of undisguised scorn, watching as she pulled them on, her fingers clumsy with haste. After a couple of seconds he followed suit, seeming to move with much less frantic speed than she employed but somehow dressing far more quickly than she could manage.

The car had already drawn to a halt as India ran downstairs, smoothing her ruffled hair with one hand and the skirt of the red dress with the other. Aidan followed her silently, showing no sign of sharing her rattled lack of composure.

They were barely back in the library before the front door opened and she heard Marion Marchant's excited voice.

'India, darling! It's great news! Your father is so much better. They say he should be home any day now.'

'That's wonderful!'

It was an effort to match her mother's delight. Obviously she was overjoyed to think of her father being finally on the mend. But other more uncomfortable events were uppermost in her mind.

'Payment in kind,' Aidan had said, making it painfully clear just how he saw her actions. Once again he had interpreted them in the worst way possible.

'We're hoping for the weekend. Of course, it will be a long, slow job before he's fully right, but— Oh!'

Alerted by the sudden exclamation, India followed her mother's gaze to see what had stopped her conversation in mid-flow.

Her heart seemed to stop dead in shock, driving all the breath from her lungs as she spotted the small dark blue box that still lay on the table where Aidan had dropped it. The lid was open to reveal the brilliant diamond ring inside.

'Oh, India! Does this mean what I think it does?'

Bright with excitement and hope, her blue-eyed gaze went from India to Aidan and back again.

'Please say that it does! It would make everything so perfect.'

'We...' India began, but could get no further. She found it impossible to think, let alone form any possible reply.

'We've been found out, Princess,' Aidan inserted quickly, his voice as smooth as the smile he switched on, his look warning her silently not to contradict him.

He needn't have worried. If she had been incapable of speech before, now her brain seemed to have blown a fuse, making her feel as if everything was being communicated to her via some sort of scrambling device, so that nothing made any sense at all. He couldn't mean...

But it seemed that Aidan did mean just what she most feared.

'We'll have to confess now, darling,' he said softly. 'I know you would have preferred to wait, but your mother's caught us out.'

Moving to slide an arm around her waist, he turned to

Marion, his expression sobering to one of apparent sincerity.

'I asked India to marry me, give me a second chance to make her happy.'

That grip on her waist might have looked casual, gently loving, but appearances were definitely deceptive. When India stiffened, making a move to protest, it tightened punishingly, reducing her attempt at speech to a muffled grunt of discomfort.

Disbelievingly, she heard Aidan continue, 'She said yes.'

'Oh, *darlings,* I'm so pleased!'

Gathered close into her mother's suffocating hug, India struggled to gather her whirling thoughts and rearrange them in some sort of order. At least she had a couple of seconds' grace like this, her face completely hidden by the strength of Aidan's shoulder crushed tightly against her.

The casual ease with which Aidan had spoken, that wide, relaxed smile, told their own story, one that made the poison of bitterness run like acid through her veins. How could he be so relaxed, so composed about everything, when he was lying through his teeth? But of course there was no need for him to show any emotion, because the real truth was that he had none at all to show.

Reluctantly her thoughts went back to the fiery passion they had just shared, the wild, physical pleasure that had seemed to her to speak of so much more than pure lust. It had to mean more than that, she had told herself. But deep down she had known that it was only self-deception.

'It will do for now,' Aidan had said, making it plain that, for him, the physical pleasure was quite sufficient. But India had been driven by love and the hope of it being reciprocated, and, acknowledging that, she knew she could never settle for passion without love—even if it meant losing him for ever.

And now this. The first time he had asked her to marry him it had been simply because he had thought that was what she wanted, that without it she wouldn't continue their relationship. There had been no love in it, nothing more than desire, and there was no such feeling in him now. He was simply acting to conceal the truth from her mother, unaware of, or certainly not caring about, the pain he was inflicting in the process.

'We must celebrate! I'm sure I've got some champagne somewhere!'

'Isn't it a bit early for that?' India forced the words past the knot in her throat.

To her astonishment, Aidan came to her rescue.

'You'll have us all roaring drunk!' he protested mildly, making India blink in disbelief at the warm humour in his tone. 'No one's eaten since lunchtime. Why don't we settle for tea now, and save the champagne for when your husband is home?'

'Of course; he should share in this.' Marion allowed herself to be dissuaded. 'Tea it is, then.'

Her steps light, she headed for the kitchen. As soon as she was out of earshot, India rounded on the man beside her.

'You've gone too far this time! I won't be a party to this.'

'No?' Aidan questioned satirically. 'It seems to me it's too late for such a protest. You had your chance to say no and didn't take it.'

'Chance!' India echoed hollowly. 'I had no chance, and you know it. And now I'm stuck with this hateful deception...'

As she swallowed the words down, realising too late how much they admitted defeat, Aidan picked up the ring box, toying with it idly. For a long moment he studied the ring inside, then turned to India, his expression unreadable, his dark eyes hooded.

'You'd better wear this, I suppose.'

'I can't.'

Once before Aidan had given her that ring, with a proposal of marriage that she now knew to have been as false as the story he had just told her mother. The pain she had endured following his rejection of her then would be as nothing when compared with the agony of letting him give it to her again now, in the full knowledge that it was a coldly, callously calculated action meant only to further his own cruel ends.

'Your mother is hardly likely to believe in our engagement if you don't,' Aidan pointed out with icy calm.

But India could only shake her head silently. A moment later he drew in a sharp breath, as if coming to a decision.

'If it makes it any easier for you, we could make it for real.'

'For...?' India's head came up sharply, her eyes dark with shock and disbelief. 'You can't mean...'

'If you're worried about it being a lie, I really could propose again, and you could—'

But she had to stop him there, couldn't bear to let him continue. If he did she might hear something she would actually be tempted to consider.

He didn't mean it, she knew. He *couldn't* mean it. Not Aidan, who had vowed only ever to marry someone he truly loved.

'Don't be ridiculous!' Panic made her voice high and tight. 'Could you really think of marrying when there isn't love on both sides?'

His silence in response to the question said it all without a word having to be spoken. Any hope that India had let into her weak, desperate heart died in that silence, finally shrivelling into dust as he shook his dark head firmly.

'No,' he said with terrible finality. 'I said I never would and I've no intention of going back on that.'

'And neither could I—so don't ever talk to me of marriage again.' The pain pushed her into a bitter acidity that she prayed hid the way she was slowly tearing to pieces inside. 'You may have trapped me into this pretence, but that's all it is—a sham, a foul, hateful lie.'

'Fine.'

Aidan tossed the ring back down onto the table. The look he turned on her face was opaque and blank, the total lack of emotion telling its own story.

'If that's the way you feel, then I couldn't agree more.'

CHAPTER THIRTEEN

'AIDAN?'

India put her head round the door into the library. This was where Aidan always seemed to shut himself away these days.

Sure enough, he was once more at the big desk, though today without the usual thick layer of papers that made it look as if a heavy snowfall had covered the surface before him. Instead, there was just one large white envelope on which he had been writing, his hand stilling at the sound of her voice.

'We're leaving for the hospital now, to collect Dad.'

He barely lifted his head to acknowledge her, and India bit her lower lip hard at the thought that this distant, sombre face was the only one that he had showed since the moment, four days before, when her mother had surprised them and seen the engagement ring.

He only joined the family for the evening meal, when he ate little and said less, and had strictly avoided any opportunity of being left alone with her.

The engagement ring had disappeared, with all the other things she had tried to return to him, and he had offered no explanation of the reason why she wasn't wearing it. It had been left to India herself to come up with the muddled excuse of it no longer fitting properly and needing alteration when her mother had noted its absence.

The memory of how he had looked as she had stammered out this story made her blood run cold in her veins. His eyes dark with contempt, his expression coldly aloof, he had been as distant and unemotional as some marble statue.

He wore the same expression now, she realised. Even the

passion that had once been such a vital part of their relationship seemed to have died, dowsed by some icy jet of loathing.

'I—don't expect we'll be more than an hour or so.'

'Fine.' It was a curt dismissal. But then Aidan seemed to reconsider. 'Oh, and India…'

He reached out and picked up the envelope from the desk in front of him, holding it out to her.

'Give that to your father, will you?'

'To my father?'

Her expression puzzled, India slowly crossed the room and took the envelope, her frown deepening as she felt its thickness.

'What is this?'

'Just something he'll know how to handle.'

'But why now?'

A sudden spasm of fear made her heart kick painfully, and her fingers clenched on the white vellum she held. Was it possible? Could Aidan really be so cruel?

'Aidan, he's only just out of hospital! He's not really well…'

Her voice died before the blaze in his eyes, the flaring rejection of the thoughts she hadn't been able to put into words but which he had read as easily as if she were an open book.

'God, Princess, do you really think I am capable of that?'

With a violent movement he pushed his chair back and got to his feet. He swung away from her towards the window, every inch of his long body stiff with rejection of her, his hands pushed deep into the pockets of his black trousers almost as if he didn't trust himself not to use them.

'Do you truly believe that I would use a sick man…?'

He didn't need to finish the sentence. In that moment before he had turned away from her, India had seen such a rawness of feeling on his face that she could have no possible doubts.

'No. Aidan, I'm sorry.'

But even as she spoke the words it struck her that that was precisely what he had wanted her to believe all along. He had made it seem as if he was prepared to take his revenge on her father by reducing him to bankruptcy and taking over his beloved family home. But his reaction now seemed to deny the truth of the scenario he had been at such pains to set up.

'Aidan?'

And now, when she was least prepared, least able to cope with it, she was suddenly swamped with the most intense physical awareness of the sensual impact of the man before her.

Only now did she realise how much his distance of the past days had cost her. She had missed his touch, his caress, his kiss. Her whole body ached with a sense of loss, of yearning to bridge the gap between them in the most primitive, passionate way.

Having known how it felt to become truly one and complete with this man, she now felt so empty and lost that it was like a raw pain in her heart. It was as if some vital, basic part of her had been torn away and all that was left was an ugly, bleeding wound.

'I'm sorry,' she said again, then flinched back as he whirled round.

'For God's sake, India,' Aidan snarled. 'Get out of here. Take that letter and give it to your father, and leave me in peace!'

Her tongue seemed to have frozen in her mouth. She couldn't form any response—but then, there was nothing she could say. Anything she tried, any word or gesture, would be violently repulsed, she knew.

Pushing the letter into the pocket of her red linen jacket, she turned and headed for the door. The short journey seemed to take a lifetime, every second of it burdened by an intense awareness of his eyes watching her, his gaze seeming to bore into her back so that she felt it might actually burn into her skin.

Her hand was on the door when suddenly Aidan spoke again.

'India.'

It was a very different voice. His use of her name was strangely soft, almost gentle, and it had her turning swiftly, the immediacy of her response betraying her sensitivity to him.

Something in his voice, in the darkness of his eyes, grated over her nerves. Perhaps it was the sunlight behind him, but suddenly his expression looked tense and drawn.

'Yes?'

But even as she spoke a dramatic change took place in Aidan's face. Every trace of tension was smoothed away, as if his features were a photograph that had been carefully airbrushed.

'Take care.'

The words were tossed at her, thrown away with such indifference that they had a bite like the most concentrated acid. She must have been hearing things a moment before. That other, strangely vulnerable Aidan could not possibly have existed.

'Of course I will,' she assured him blithely, switching on a smile that concealed the pain of her shattered heart. 'I'll be back before you have time to miss me.'

'Impossible,' Aidan returned enigmatically. 'Goodbye, Princess.'

She had been dismissed. But still some lingering doubt, some sense of unease had her lingering uncertainly. When she didn't move, Aidan looked up sharply, with a frown of displeasure drawing his brows together.

'I said *goodbye*, India.' His tone threatened retribution if she didn't obey. 'And don't forget to give that letter to your father.'

She had no alternative but to leave, hurrying to the car where her mother and Gary were waiting.

She had been imagining things, she told herself firmly. *Aidan*—vulnerable? Impossible! He was impregnable as a medieval castle; nothing could pierce that armour of self-assurance he wore so easily.

So why could she not get his face out of her mind? Why did it linger in her thoughts like a reproach, unnerving and unsettling her, making it impossible to concentrate? It fretted at her memory so that she seemed to be only half in the present, attending to the preparations for her father's departure from hospital with a vague lack of concentration that was most unlike her.

It was only when they were about to leave the ward that she remembered something else. 'Oh, Dad, I almost forgot—this is for you.'

The first frisson of doubt shivered down her spine as she watched her father open the envelope. Another, stronger twist of apprehension followed as he scanned the type-written words, a look of blank incomprehension on his face.

'I—don't understand.' The words came with difficulty, his speech not fully back to normal. 'Why has Aidan Wolfe—?'

He broke off, shaking his head in confusion.

'Aidan's been staying with us,' Marion put in hastily. They had agreed to tell him this today, but had planned on waiting till they got home. 'He and India have made it up.'

'Is that why...?'

'What is it, Dad?' India asked urgently as her father's eyes went to her face. 'What has Aidan done?'

'The house—everything. He's written off all I ever owed him.'

'He's...'

India couldn't believe she had heard him right. Ignoring her mother's bewildered questions, she reached for the letter, her eyes flying over the print.

All debts written off... The Grange returned to the Marchant family... All repairs and renovations Aidan's gift to them.

'Aidan...'

How could he be so generous? *Why* should he give them

so much when he had them in his power? But then, in her mind, she could hear Aidan's voice when he had talked of the swimming pool.

'I thought it would be good for your father,' he'd said.

Once again she heard her own voice, 'Would you do that for him?'

And Aidan's dismissive reply.

She couldn't think, couldn't work out just what all this meant. She only knew that the one thing in her thoughts was the image of those last moments with Aidan in the library before she had left.

She saw again that disturbing, uncharacteristic look on his face, heard the emphasis on that final *'Goodbye'*.

Her mother had been watching her closely, and saw the way her daughter's face changed.

'India, if there's something you have to do, then don't worry about us,' she said with intuitive understanding. 'There'll be an ambulance to take us home.'

India flashed her a deeply grateful glance.

'I *have* to go! Dad, I'm sorry—but this is important. Perhaps the most important thing in my life.'

She was moving even as she spoke, flinging open the door in a rush, barely hearing the words her father called after her. She ran along seemingly never-ending corridors, down echoing stairs, not daring to wait for the lift, dashing out of the main exit and sprinting across the car park.

She drove like a rally driver back towards Westbury, praying all the time that she was wrong, that Aidan's behaviour hadn't meant what she thought. But when she reached the roundabout on the outskirts of the village she was forced to screech down to a crawl behind a large, slow-moving caravan.

'Oh, come on, come *on!*' she muttered furiously, her fingers tapping restlessly on the steering wheel.

The frantic movements stilled, freezing suddenly as she saw an all too familiar car pass on the inner lane of the roundabout.

'Aidan!'

She'd know the sleek, dark lines of his car anywhere—and that lane led to the turn-off for the motorway!

So she had guessed right. Aidan was going back to London, without a word of explanation. So what did she do now? she asked herself as the caravan moved off at last.

She wasn't going to let him go without a fight, that was for sure! She didn't know what had been going through his mind when he had written that letter to her father, and the only way to find out was to tackle him face to face.

As soon as the thought had entered her mind, India turned it into action, swinging her car into the same lane that Aidan had used and putting her foot down hard once she was on the straight again. Perhaps she could catch him up, make him stop before he got onto the motorway. One thing was sure—she was going to have this out with him if she had to follow him all the way to London.

At last the Jaguar came into sight ahead of her. Aidan didn't appear to have noticed her presence on his tail, or, if he had, he wasn't taking the expected action of speeding up in order to get away from her. Instead, very much to her surprise, he actually seemed to be slowing down.

'What now?'

Frowning her confusion, India adjusted her own speed, staying well behind the grey car. Was he not heading for the motorway after all? Had she simply over-reacted, building up fears that didn't really exist?

No, she hadn't been wrong. Even from this distance she could see the outline of a suitcase on the back seat of the car ahead. That wasn't her imagination.

He was turning now. So where…?

And then realisation dawned. The grey car was coming to a halt outside a painfully familiar building. Aidan had parked outside the local church, the place where he and India should have been married the year before.

Sudden tears blurred India's eyes, her heart lurching into a ragged, uneven beat that had her hands clenching on the wheel, waiting for the moment of reaction to pass. Could this really be happening? And, what was more, could it possibly mean what she thought—what she hoped more than anything in the world—it could?

Blinking hard to clear her vision, she watched as Aidan got out of the car, waiting until he had made his way up the path before she slid her own vehicle behind his, coming to a halt and pulling on the brake. He still hadn't seen her, seemed unaware of her presence. But all the same she found herself hurrying after him, fearful he might get away from her.

After the bright sunlight of the afternoon, the interior of the church was cool and dim, and she had to struggle to focus her gaze clearly enough to see where Aidan was. At last she saw him, at the far end of the aisle.

He was just standing silently, tall and dark in the black trousers and shirt he had worn that morning, hands deep in his pockets as he stared at the altar where just over twelve months before they had stood together, ready to take their vows.

Because his back was to her, there was no way that India could judge his expression, and so his mood. But something about the set of his shoulders, the dark head slightly bent, was so expressive of defeat and depression that it wrenched at her heart, making her take a couple of hasty steps towards him.

'Aidan?'

Her voice was just a croak, barely audible, but he heard it and spun round at once. Shock, surprise and something else, something raw and uncontrolled, flashed across his carved features just for a second. But almost immediately his face closed up again, that smoothing effect being used once more in order to erase the revealing expression.

But this time the technique wasn't quite so successful. For one thing India had seen it before, and so she was alert to the signs of control that didn't quite match with the nonchalance he was trying to display. And for another she

could see the tension at the corners of his mouth, the shadowed eyes, the tightness of skin across his cheekbones and
round the clenched jaw.

'What the hell are you doing here?' he demanded
harshly.

It was hardly the most welcoming response, and the
dark-eyed, baleful glare that accompanied it was thoroughly
unnerving. But India drew on all her resolve in order not
to be intimidated. Swallowing hard, she drew a deep, calm-
ing breath.

'I followed you from the roundabout. I had to talk to
you.'

'We've nothing to say to each other.'

'Oh, yes, we have. Or, at least, if you've nothing to say
to me, I've plenty I want to ask you. Such as, where were
you going, Aidan? Were you on your way back to
London?'

The questions that had been burning in her brain tumbled
out one after the other. She needed the answers too urgently
now to be able to hold them back.

'Were you leaving, Aidan? Is that it?'

He didn't answer, keeping stubbornly silent, his features
still set in those hard, unyielding lines. But he couldn't hide
the momentary flash of some unsettled feeling in his eyes,
and it was that which gave India her answer.

'It is, isn't it? But why?'

'I thought it was for the best.'

'The best?' Disbelievingly, India echoed his emotionless
statement. 'The best for who, Aidan? For you or for me?'

'For both of us. We should never be together. I should
have seen that we were wrong for each other from the
start—that we would only tear ourselves apart.'

His words held such harsh conviction that, hearing them,
India felt her blood turn to ice. Every trace of hope and
belief drained from her mind, leaving just a hollow, desolate ache in its place.

'You shouldn't have come after me, India. I don't want

you here. I want you to keep well away from me. Stay out of my life—is that understood?'

How much more clearly could he spell it out? She'd got it all wrong. He had never felt anything for her in the first place, and, if it was possible, he now felt even less.

'Oh, yes,' she said brokenly. 'I understand perfectly.'

'Good. So, now that we've got that sorted out, I'm going and I don't want you to follow me.'

And if she hadn't already got the message loud and clear then the way he stalked past, his long body held stiffly away from her so that there was no chance of their touching, would have made it painfully plain. It was as if he felt that the slightest contact between them would contaminate him—and that was more than enough to convince even her foolish heart.

Aidan didn't want her; he never had. She had only been fooling herself all along. And her frantic dash to find him, that desperate drive from the hospital, had just been a wild-goose chase after all.

CHAPTER FOURTEEN

'I'M GOING and I don't want you to follow me... Stay out of my life...'

Aidan's words couldn't have been clearer, the harsh tones he had used leaving India without a trace of hope in her heart. She knew that if she was fool enough to try to call him back he would only rebuff her with a violence that would tear her already desolated heart into tiny, irreparable pieces.

But she couldn't stop herself from turning to watch him, and in that moment something changed. It was as if she had slipped into a time warp, with the present becoming the past. It might almost have been her wedding day all over again, with her watching the man she loved walk away from her, facing that anguish all over again.

She couldn't let it happen! But what could she do to stop it?

In the back of her mind she heard once more the sound of Aidan's voice. 'If you ask the right questions, I'll answer.'

But what were the *right* questions? In the face of his implacable rejection of her, what could she possibly do? And was there any point in doing *anything*?

But wasn't she really forgetting the obvious? What about the reason why she was here in the first place?

'Aidan! Wait!'

Her cry reached him just as he put one hand on the door. He stilled immediately, but he didn't turn. Instead he just waited, keeping his head stubbornly averted.

'I—have some questions to ask you. If, after you answer them, you still want to go, then I won't try to stop you. But I need complete honesty from you. If you give me the truth, then I'll do the same for you.'

But that honesty might cost her far more than she was prepared for, she warned herself. She was taking a terrible risk.

The sense of fearful apprehension that tightened every nerve was in no way eased by Aidan's exasperated sigh before, slowly and with obvious reluctance, he turned back to her at last.

'Ask away,' he growled discouragingly.

India drew a deep, shaken breath. She had her chance. She had to take it.

'I gave your letter to my father.'

Her green eyes searched his set face, looking for any hint of reaction but finding none. He was determined not to help her.

'Why did you do that, Aidan? What made you write off all his debts like that?'

'I can afford it.'

The answer came too pat, accompanied by a careless shrug of the shoulders. It was a throwaway line, meant to deter further questions. She couldn't let it distract her from her purpose.

'I said *honesty*, Aidan!' she flashed fiercely. 'We'll never get anywhere if you don't play it straight.'

'And is there anywhere for us to go?'

The bleak cynicism of his retort almost unnerved her.

'I don't know,' she sighed wearily. 'I only know that we have no chance at all if you won't even try. You said we didn't really know each other before…' In desperation she made her last appeal, emerald eyes pleading with him to listen. 'Doesn't that make you want to try harder this time?'

'Not really.'

His expression and stance were as hard and unyielding as the stone carvings of the baptismal font behind him. His eyes seemed as blank and unfocused as those of the statues of the saints on the walls. India felt that she was having as much effect on him as if she were banging her head hard against those decorations.

'I told you, I don't bet on losers.'

'And this has no chance at all?'

'Of course it doesn't! It was a non-runner from the start, only I was too blind to see that. I've been all sorts of a fool recently. A fool to try and revive our relationship when there's nothing there to bring back to life. I was wrong even to come back to Westbury. I should have known that seeking you out—'

Some tiny movement, a response she couldn't quite control, made him stop dead. In the split second before he realised what he'd said and heavy lids hooded his eyes, hiding all the trace of feeling from her, she caught a glimpse of something else, something very different and very revealing. A tiny flare of reaction that told her she had finally found a chink in that apparently impregnable armour.

'*Seeking me out,*' she said carefully, struggling to keep her voice calm. 'But you said you came to see my father. That you wanted payment for his debts, nothing more.'

There it was again, that same, faint flicker in an otherwise steady, cold-eyed gaze. But Aidan was too strong, too determined to reveal much.

India felt as if she was groping her way through thick, clinging fog. There was just the suggestion of a path beneath her feet, but it was rough and potholed, and she found it difficult to get any sort of foothold on it. At any moment it might crumble away, leaving her without any support whatsoever.

'But of course, that's just a myth, isn't it, Aidan?' She prayed she sounded more confident than she actually felt. 'Men like you don't come debt-collecting. You have employees to do that for you. You could have stayed snug in London and put it all in the hands of some capable minion...'

'I wanted the Grange.'

A new note in his voice told her that, if he was not exactly on the retreat, Aidan had definitely reached the point where the balance of the situation seemed to be slipping away from him.

'Oh, yes. You wanted the Grange so much that you spent a fortune on all those repairs. You set about lovingly restoring it to its former glory—improving it beyond all recognition, in fact—and then you handed it back to my father without a second thought.'

Aidan's back might not be physically up against the heavy wooden door behind him, but mentally at least he was cornered, and they both knew it. With a sudden surge of confidence, India pressed home her advantage.

'So tell me, Aidan, is that the action of a ruthless businessman with the sort of reputation that you have been so careful to build up over the years? Is that the sort of thing the Lone Wolfe would do?'

At last Aidan's head came up, ebony eyes flashing violent rejection of her words.

'You know I've always hated that damned nickname!'

'Why? Because it's not you?'

'It might seem that way on the outside, but inside...'

'Inside?' India prompted, when he let the sentence trail off.

'Inside is a bloody fool who's crazily in love with a woman who doesn't love him back!' Aidan flashed. 'That is most definitely not the sort of thing the Lone Wolfe is supposed to do!'

Then, looking into India's face in the stunned silence that followed, he gave a wryly twisted smile and shrugged dismissively.

'Well, you said you wanted honesty.'

'I...'

India couldn't find a word to say. She was too busy struggling to absorb the full impact of his declaration. *Had* he said *crazily in love*?

'All right, I've gone this far; I might as well give you the full story.' The aggression in Aidan's tone didn't square with the look in his eyes. 'I fell in love with you in the first moment I saw you, when you came up to me at that party.'

'But—what I said—the bet...'

'I didn't realise you were the woman I'd overheard—not at first. By the time it dawned on me, I was already lost. I tried to tell myself that I would just teach you a lesson. That I would play you along so far and then drop you hard from a very great height. But deep down I knew I was just fooling myself, that I could never do it. When you said you wanted marriage I just grabbed at the chance.'

'And threw it back in my face on our wedding day!'

'I know…'

One long hand raked through his dark hair in a gesture that revealed the unease he had managed to keep out of his voice.

'India, I told you—I meant to marry you. I *wanted* to marry you, but I didn't know your feelings.'

'I never said, did I?' She had been too scared, too unsure of *him*. 'But I did say yes to marriage.'

'Oh, yes, and I knew why. You wanted me because I was rich and because we were good together in bed. I convinced myself that that was enough. But that day in the church, when I looked at you, it really came home to me just what I was trying to do.'

'And what was that?' India put in apprehensively when he hesitated.

'I was trying to tie you down, lock you into a marriage that wasn't really based on love. I wanted to have you in my life, hold onto you however I could and never let you go, but I wasn't thinking straight. It wasn't until I realised that that was exactly what had happened to my parents that I saw just how our marriage would end up in the future. I knew then I had to let you go.'

'You did more than that.' In spite of all she did to stop it, some trace of the hurt she had felt then still lingered under the words.

'I know.' It was very soft. 'But I couldn't think what else to do. I had to make sure that you stayed away from me. If you had come after me I wouldn't have been able to handle it. If I'd seen you again I wouldn't have been able to resist you, so I had to finish it once and for all. I couldn't trap you in a marriage like the one my parents had, couldn't face the possibility that you'd end up hating me as my mother hated my father.'

'If I'd really wanted to hurt you, it would have been far crueller to have gone ahead and married you.' Aidan's words from days ago rang inside India's head with a new and much more powerful impact.

'So I had to set you free.'

Set you free. She had never looked at his actions in that light before, but, now that she did, they seemed so honest, so wonderfully generous—so *loving*.

And he had been prepared to do it all over again, this time. He would actually have walked away, leaving her—and her father—freer than ever before, with all their debts cleared and the Grange beautifully restored.

'Aidan,' she put in quietly, 'you're forgetting one very important thing.'

'What's that?' He frowned his confusion, dark eyes clouded.

'Your parents never really loved each other—not properly. They didn't even know what love is—not the way that we do.'

Aidan became very still, his face pale, skin drawn tight across the strong cheekbones.

'"We"?' he questioned hoarsely.

'That's right.' India took a couple of unsteady steps towards him, holding out a hand to him. 'Don't you know? I love you too.'

If he held back any longer she knew that her self-control would shatter, splintering her composure into tiny, hopeless pieces. But the next moment Aidan had crossed the space between them swiftly, gathering her up into his arms and crushing her close.

His kiss was all she had ever dreamed of. In it was all the longing and pain of the past year, but there too was the new hope, the passion they shared. And above all else the love she now knew he felt.

It was a long, long time before he lifted his head, still

holding her tight. Gently he led her to one of the pews, drawing her down onto the wooden seat beside him.

'Is it true?' His voice was low and shaken. 'Is it really true that you love me? I didn't imagine you saying that?'

'No, you didn't imagine a thing. You heard me perfectly. I love you, Aidan, with all my heart. And please believe me that your money means nothing to me. I would love you if you were poor—if you had nothing. You are all that matters to me.'

'In spite of all I've—' Aidan began, but India silenced him with a gentle touch of her fingers across his mouth.

'Warts and all, remember?' she told him softly, earning herself another long, deeply sensual kiss.

'I've been so blind.' Aidan shook his dark head at the thought of his own foolishness. 'I don't know why I didn't see.'

'Perhaps because of the way your parents were. You didn't know what you were looking for. And of course didn't help with that stupid bet.'

'I made some distorted assumptions as a result of that. judged you on some badly flawed evidence, and because of that I believed your father when he said you wanted a pre-nuptial agreement.'

'You should have talked to me.' There was no reproach in her words, just a thread of sadness.

'I *know*—believe me, I know. But to tell the truth I didn't dare. I was afraid if I did you'd come right out and say you didn't love me, that you only wanted my money. And at the time it seemed so in character—the character I believed you were. I would have done *anything* at all to keep you in my life.'

'So why did you put those conditions on the agreement? Why did you tie it up for a year?'

'Because I still planned to marry you. I wanted you whatever agreement you or, as it turned out, your father wanted to draw up. I had the vain hope that you thought you'd soon be rich enough not to need a wealthy husband, then the money element would have been taken out of the equation. I hoped to use the year's grace to really get to know you, and, hopefully, make you fall in love with me so that when it was up you'd stay.'

'And this time?' At last it seemed that she was finding the right questions to ask, and the answers were everything she could have hoped for and more. 'Why did you come back?'

Those dark eyes turned to her in a look that gave her her answer without a word having to be spoken. But still Aidan went on.

'To find you. I'd tried to stay away, but I couldn't. I couldn't live without you. All I had was an existence, nothing more. I reasoned that by now you'd have access to the money and perhaps we could start again on a more equal footing. But you wanted nothing to do with me—and who could blame you? I didn't know how to get through to you, so when your father's debts came due I just snatched at the chance it gave me.'

'You would never have called in my father's debts.'

It was a statement, not a question, but all the same she saw Aidan's head move in vehement denial.

'I told myself I'd use those gambling debts to give me a hold over him—but the truth was that really they gave me an excuse to come back, to see you. I wanted to see your father to try and work things out, but finding out that, legally, I was now the owner of the Grange seemed like fate playing into my hands. It was the only way I could think of to stay in your life long enough to work things out.'

One strong hand raked through the silk of his hair in a gesture that was eloquently expressive of the way he was feeling.

'And then, when I realised how honest and straight you really were... India, darling, I'm so sorry...'

'Don't.' She kissed the apology from his lips. 'Dad behaved so badly, using you like that, interfering in our lives. Do you think you can ever forgive him?'

'If you love me, I can do anything. He's your family,

and you love him, so for your sake I'll put the past behind us. I just wonder if he...'

'You don't have to worry,' India put in hastily, the memory of her father's reaction suddenly surfacing in her mind. 'When I came after you, I'm sure Dad guessed where I was going, and approved. I'm certain he's ready to tell you that he's made some appalling mistakes and will be grateful for a chance to put things right.'

'Then I'll meet him more than halfway.'

'Aidan...' She couldn't put her thoughts into words, but her glowing face and the emerald brilliance of her eyes told their own story, making him smile softly.

'I'd do anything for you, my beautiful love. I want to spend the rest of my life making you happy. Talking of which—come with me.'

'Where...?' India cried as he took her hand, pulling her gently to her feet.

'Wait a moment.' He hushed her. 'You'll see.'

He led her out of the pew and slowly back down the aisle towards the altar. At the foot of the steps where they had stood a year before he paused and turned, his hand tightening on hers and his eyes very deep and dark.

'India, my darling, this seems the most appropriate place to ask this. Will you marry me? Properly this time? Will you give me the chance to show how deep and true my love for you really is? Will you let me spend the rest of my life making up for this lost year, and making every other year we spend together the happiest you've ever experienced?'

'Do you have to ask?' India sighed her happiness.

'Perhaps not, but I certainly need an answer. I vowed never to marry until I was sure that I truly loved and was loved in return. I have no doubts now; my only future is with you. Without you, I'm nothing. So please say—'

'Yes!' India broke in. 'Oh, Aidan, of course the answer's yes. It could never be anything else.'

A sudden thought struck her, widening her eyes and curling the corners of her mouth into a delighted smile.

'What is it?' Aidan had caught her change of mood.

'I was remembering the way you caught the bouquet. You said that traditionally it meant that you'd be the next one to marry—and you were right. Out of the guests that day, you'll be the next one down the aisle.'

'Which, if I'm honest, was exactly what I was praying for even then.'

His smile faded, his eyes looking deep into hers, his love burning there, clear for her to see.

'Oh, God, India,' he said huskily. 'Come here and kiss me!'

Willingly she went into his arms, her face already lifted for his kiss. Once more she was crushed against his strength, held so tightly that she could have no hope of breaking free. Not that she wanted to. This was where she belonged, where she would spend the rest of her future.

Aidan's kiss took her lips with a gentleness that seemed to draw her soul from her body. But a second later his mood had changed completely, becoming warmly sensual, then deeply, demandingly passionate, his hands moving over her body in a way that set every one of her senses alight.

'Oh, God, India!' Aidan muttered against her lips. 'The way you make me feel is not at all appropriate to where we are. My thoughts are definitely not fitting for a church.'

India turned wide, innocent green eyes on his face, noting the glitter in his own eyes, the wash of colour in his cheeks.

'Really?' she teased. 'And where would they be fitting?'

'You know, you little witch! You don't need me to tell you.'

'No,' India agreed, running her hand slowly down his body until it came to rest on the leather belt that encircled his narrow waist. 'But I think it's time we found somewhere more suitable, so that you can show me.'

And with their fingers laced tightly together they walked hand in hand away from the past and into a bright, loving future.

MILLS & BOON®

Next Month's Romances

♡

Each month you can choose from a wide variety of romance novels from Mills & Boon. Below are the new titles to look out for next month from the Presents™ and Enchanted™ series.

Presents™

A NANNY FOR CHRISTMAS	Sara Craven
A FORBIDDEN DESIRE	Robyn Donald
THE WINTER BRIDE	Lynne Graham
THE PERFECT MATCH?	Penny Jordan
RED-HOT AND RECKLESS	Miranda Lee
BARGAIN WITH THE WIND	Kathleen O'Brien
THE DISOBEDIENT BRIDE	Elizabeth Power
ALL MALE	Kay Thorpe

Enchanted™

SANTA'S SPECIAL DELIVERY	Val Daniels
THE MARRIAGE PACT	Elizabeth Duke
A MIRACLE FOR CHRISTMAS	Grace Green
ACCIDENTAL WIFE	Day Leclaire
ONE NIGHT BEFORE CHRISTMAS	Catherine Leigh
A SINGULAR HONEYMOON	Leigh Michaels
A HUSBAND FOR CHRISTMAS	Emma Richmond
TEMPORARY GIRLFRIEND	Jessica Steele

LaVyrle
SPENCER

✳

The Hellion

Two Hearts...Worlds Apart

As teenagers they had shared a wild and reckless love—and had been forced to pay the highest price. Now, three broken marriages later, Tommy Lee Gentry has come knocking on Rachel Hollis' door, begging to be given another another chance.

"LaVyrle Spencer has written a truly special story...The Hellion is nostalgic and captures the feelings of love lost and years wasted...SUPERB!"

—Chicago Sun Times

MIRA®

AVAILABLE IN PAPERBACK FROM NOVEMBER 1997

GET TO KNOW

THE BEST OF ENEMIES

the latest blockbuster from TAYLOR SMITH

Who would you trust with your life? Think again.

*Linked to a terrorist bombing, a young student goes
missing. One woman believes in the girl's innocence
and is determined to find her before she is silenced.
Leya Nash has to decide—quickly—who to trust.
The wrong choice could be fatal.*

Valid only in the UK & Ireland against purchases made in retail outlets
and not in conjunction with any Reader Service or other offer.

50ᵖ OFF
COUPON
VALID UNTIL: 28.2.1998

TAYLOR SMITH'S *THE BEST OF ENEMIES*

9 904170 200509

0472 00189